'This isn't fun...

She was as far away... could get but notic... sheets from him so that they now rested low on his abdomen.

He had a fabulous body, broad-shouldered with a powerful chest. Before she could stop herself her eyes slipped further down to the hard, flat stomach, and then lower. The thought that they had both been lying naked next to each other all night made her temperature rise wildly.

'Do you like what you see?' Rogan asked with a grin. 'I know I do.'

Quickly she lay down again and glared at him from the other pillow. 'The joke's gone far enough, Rogan. I want you out of my bed.'

'As I was here first, strictly speaking, you're in my bed.' He made no move at all. 'You must have come to the wrong bedroom last night…or maybe the right one, depending on how you want to look at it.'

'If you are trying to say that I deliberately came to your bed then you couldn't be more mistaken.'

He rolled over and leaned on his elbow to look at her, wry humour in his dark eyes. 'Are you sure?' he whispered seductively.

Kathryn Ross was born in Zambia where her parents happened to live at that time. Educated in Ireland and England, she now lives in a village near Blackpool, Lancashire. Kathryn is a professional beauty therapist, but writing is her first love. As a child she wrote adventure stories and at thirteen was editor of her school magazine. Happily, ten writing years later DESIGNED WITH LOVE was accepted by Mills & Boon. A romantic Sagittarian, she loves travelling to exotic locations.

Recent titles by the same author:

BRIDE FOR A YEAR

THE BOSS'S MISTRESS

BY
KATHRYN ROSS

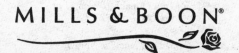

MILLS & BOON®

First published in Great Britain 1998
Harlequin Mills & Boon Limited,
Eton House, 18-24 Paradise Road, Richmond, Surrey TW9 1SR

© Kathryn Ross 1998

ISBN 0 263 81223 5

Set in Times Roman 10½ on 11 pt.
01-9811-52537 C1

Printed and bound in Norway
by AiT Trondheim AS, Trondheim

CHAPTER ONE

THE October day was drawing in early. It was only four-thirty and already a dark mist was settling over the River Liffey and the lights of Dublin twinkled in the dusky glow of the approaching evening.

Laura turned her car down the street that led to her office. She had just been out to the McClusky residence and was feeling pleased with herself. Clara McClusky was a very satisfied client and, though she said it herself, Laura had made a very good job of the interior design for her house. It looked stunning.

She smiled. All she had to do now was type up a report and add the photographs she had taken, then she could get home for the evening—perhaps take the children out for a pizza to celebrate the successful conclusion to a major contract. Hopefully, it *was* something to celebrate and she would still have a job next week. The unbidden thought made a cloud of concern settle over her.

The company she worked for was being taken over next week and she would have a new boss. It seemed strange to think that James Design was no longer going to be a family concern. She had been working for Robert James since her husband died four years ago. The job had been a godsend, coming at a time when she'd been most in need, with two children to take care of and a mountain of debt which her husband had left behind.

Robert had been so sweet to her and had overlooked the fact that she had little practical experience in the workplace, owing to the fact that marriage and children had taken her away from her career. Instead he had concentrated on the fact that she was a very well-qualified interior designer.

Laura hadn't let him down. She had worked hard and had more than proved herself in her job, so much so that she was subsequently made senior design consultant. Now, suddenly, Laura had this awful feeling that she was going to have to prove herself all over again. She very much wanted to make a good impression with the new owner, and prayed the McClusky account would swing it for her. She really needed this job.

Robert was nearly seventy, but she had hoped that when he decided to retire he would hand over the reins of the business to his stepson, Paul, and that the company would continue to run in the same time-honoured tradition that had made the James name synonymous with quality and distinctive furnishings in Ireland.

It had come as a severe shock when Robert had announced that the company was being taken over by a big multinational corporation. Powers PLC sounded big and impersonal and, by the sound of things, the man in control was ruthless and ambitious. Laura tried to console herself that Paul was still going to be on the board of directors so there would still be some of the old family's involvement…but somehow she couldn't see Paul standing up to a multinational firm if they decided on radical changes.

Robert had mooted to her that things would probably remain the same and not to worry about her job, but that was easier said than done. Whispers about redundancies and closure had been rife for a while now in the office.

This morning the rumours had escalated with the circulation of a memo to all members of staff, telling them that the new managing director would be interviewing each of them during the coming weeks. To help matters they were asked to fill in details about themselves on the accompanying forms.

'That's it,' Laura's secretary, Sandra, had muttered woefully. 'He's going to start weeding out the staff.'

'Not necessarily,' Laura had said, trying her best to be optimistic. 'Why would he do that when James is so successful? He probably just wants to get a clearer picture of his new staff.'

'Huh! Have you seen some of the questions on here?' Sandra had flapped the form in disgust. 'The only thing it doesn't ask is how many times you visit the bathroom in a day. Mark my words, our new boss isn't a kindly, approachable gentleman like Mr James—this man is only concerned with profit margins.

'If I were you, Laura, I wouldn't bother to answer some of the questions on his form. I certainly wouldn't tell him you're a single mother—it will probably go against you. He'll think you need to take time off for the children and kick you out.'

'He couldn't do that.' Laura had been appalled by the suggestion.

'He could if he had a good enough excuse.' Sandra had been unrepentant. 'Apparently, he's ruthless.'

Scaremongering rubbish, Laura told herself again now. It had come almost as a relief to get out of the office today, away from the gloomy mood which had descended.

Her thoughts were abruptly interrupted by a black cat, darting out into the road from between parked cars. Although she wasn't going fast she knew there was no way she could stop in time as it was too close so she reacted instinctively and swerved to avoid it. The next moment there was a sickening sound of metal scratching against metal as she scraped against the side of a car which had been in the process of overtaking her.

She slammed on the brakes a sinking feeling in the pit of her stomach. The other car continued for a moment and stopped just ahead of her. She noticed with horror that it was a brand-new, shiny, black BMW. Her hand shook as she reached for her doorhandle and stepped out into the road.

A bitter wind caught her long dark hair, swirling it across her face and obscuring her view of the tall man who climbed out of the driver's side of the other car.

'I'm really sorry—' She started to apologise in a low tone but he cut across her abruptly.

'You were driving like a damn maniac.'

She noticed his American accent. It was husky and, despite the angry note, quite sexy. She swept a hand over her face to hold her hair back so that she could look at him properly.

She would have estimated him to be about five years her senior, putting him at around thirty-seven, and he was very good-looking in an autocratic, overpowering kind of way. He had dark eyes in a lean, square-jawed face. 'I am sorry,' she said again, a trifle breathlessly. She glanced at the door of his car and tried to console herself that the damage wasn't too bad, just a long, ugly scratch.

'What the hell were you playing at?' he demanded.

'A cat ran out in front of me and I didn't want to hit it.' She shrugged helplessly. 'I didn't know what else to do.'

He looked at her as if he couldn't quite believe what she had just said. For a moment his eyes raked over her, taking in the gentle light in her wide green eyes and the generous curve of her soft lips. He could smell the warm tones of her perfume on the frosty air. She smelt of summer, honeysuckle and roses. He frowned. 'I didn't see a cat.' His voice had lost some of its abrasiveness.

'Well there *was* one, I assure you,' she told him crisply. She shivered. It was too cold to stand out here arguing. 'Anyway, you needn't worry, I am insured.'

'Damn good job. I've just taken delivery of my car today,' he muttered. 'Couldn't you just have slammed on your brakes?'

She opened her handbag, searching for a pen and paper with impatient fingers. 'Believe me, I would have if I could,' she said with annoyance. 'This is going to cost me dear—I'll lose my no-claims bonus. But let's keep things in perspective. At least it was just a piece of metal that got damaged and not a living creature.'

'It's a BMW, not a piece of metal.'

She flashed him a scathing look, and unexpectedly he grinned. 'Yours is the piece of metal.'

She had to admit that her car had seen better days but it was all she could afford and she took exception to the remark. 'There's nothing wrong with Doris,' she told him loftily. 'She has never let me down yet.'

One dark eyebrow lifted and he looked more amused than ever.

There was something extremely attractive about his smile and the gleam of his eyes in the darkness. It made him appear rakish, devilishly handsome. The notion and the feeling that suddenly stirred inside her made her feel awkward.

'Doris?' he drawled wryly. 'You call your car Doris?'

She felt herself flushing to the roots of her hair as she realised what she had said. He must think her completely crazy. She had used the car's name without thinking. Her children had named it Doris and the name had kind of stuck. It was her mother's influence. Laura's mother, Cora, had always named her cars.

'Yes. Doris.' She tried to sound matter-of-fact, as if everyone gave their car a name and it wasn't just one of her family's idiosyncrasies.

Thinking about her mother made her forget her embarrassment. She glanced at her watch. She didn't want to be late home. Cora looked after the children from the time they came home from school until Laura got in from work. It was a very satisfactory arrangement. Cora loved her grandchildren's company and Laura could relax, knowing they were with someone she could whole-heartedly trust.

Her mother lived in the house next door so it didn't really matter if she was home a little late but, even so, Laura never overstepped the mark and always tried to be home on time. Now she was behind schedule and she still had to go into the office.

She scribbled down her details for him. 'Look, I've got to go. Give me a ring tomorrow and tell me how much the damage will cost. If it's not too high I might not claim on my insurance.' She swept a hand through her hair, her thoughts running to her financial situation.

He glanced at the piece of paper, before pushing it into the deep pockets of his dark overcoat. 'OK, I'll speak to you tomorrow.'

As Laura went back to her car she saw the black cat on a garden wall, watching her, his green eyes luminous in the glare of a passing car's headlights.

'Be more careful in future,' she told him sternly. 'You've just used up one of your nine lives.'

'Don't tell me you talk to Doris as well,' the man said in a droll tone as he opened the door of his car.

'I was talking to the cat.' Laura nodded towards the wall and the man followed her gaze, but the cat had gone.

He shook his head and muttered something under his breath, something she couldn't hear. Maybe it was just as well, she thought as she started her car up again. It would probably have been derisive.

She overtook him with a cursory nod of farewell.

'Where the heck have you been?' Sandra asked as she walked into her office a couple of minutes later. 'Everyone has been looking for you. Mr James wanted a word, and someone's been in to ask for your completed form three times now.'

'What form?' Laura asked distractedly as she took off her heavy overcoat and sat down behind her desk.

'The one for the profit-hungry new boss.' Sandra grinned.

'I'll fill that in over the weekend and hand it in on Monday morning,' Laura said decisively.

'It's up to you, but everyone else has handed theirs in,' Sandra said, before adding nonchalantly, 'And, apparently, the new boss is upstairs with Mr James as we speak.'

'What's he like?' Sandra had her full attention now.

'Haven't a clue. All I know is that Rosie, Mr James's secretary, was sent out for cherry buns, ready for his arrival, at four-thirty.'

Laura sighed. That was so typical of Robert James—he was so delightfully old-school and thoughtful. Things just wouldn't be the same around here without him.

'The days of cherry buns and coffee with the boss are well and truly in the past for us now.' Sandra sighed as well, and for a moment looked as if she wanted to cry.

'Look on the bright side. It will make it a lot easier for us to stick to a diet in future.' Laura smiled.

Sandra laughed and shook her head as she rose to leave. 'That's what I love about you, Laura. You always look on the positive side of things.'

The door closed behind her but Laura could still see her, walking down the corridor. The glass walls gave the feeling that one was sitting in a giant glass jardinière. Large plants broke up the modern geometric design of the place but there was little in the way of privacy. Except, of course, if you were the boss. He had a suite of offices upstairs.

She reached across and put on her desk lamp, then glanced at her watch. She hoped the new boss's sudden appearance today wouldn't delay her getting away tonight. Maybe she should take the children for pizza tomorrow night instead. Saturday was probably better than Friday night and she wanted to do some reading with Matthew before bedtime anyway.

Her eyes alighted on the photograph of her children on the desk. Joanne was so pretty, with straight blonde hair and blue eyes. She was almost thirteen now and the image of her late father. Matthew was more like Laura, dark hair and green-eyed. He was seven and a bundle of mischief.

Like most working mothers, Laura wished she could spend more time with her children. They were the most important thing in the world to her. But it was a catch twenty-two situation because she needed to work to pay the bills. The fact that she enjoyed her career made things a lot easier. She was good at her job. In fact, Robert James had come to rely on her more and more over these last few months.

The door of her office opened, for once catching her off guard. She glanced up, expecting to see Sandra again. She nearly fell off her chair as her eyes collided with those of the tall, handsome stranger whose car she had pranged earlier.

'What on earth are you doing here?' She felt her breath catch with a mixture of nerves and annoyance. Had he followed her to check up on her in case she didn't cough up for the damage to his car? The last thing she needed was a scene here in the office, with the new managing director prowling about. 'Look, this is not a good time for me. Please go away and we'll discuss the damage to your car tomorrow.'

One dark eyebrow lifted sardonically. 'But I want to talk to you now,' he said calmly.

She frowned, and out of the corner of her eye she saw Robert, walking down the corridor with another man following him who looked to be in his late fifties—obviously the new owner of the business. Her heart thumped unsteadily. 'Please,' she implored. 'I'm under a lot of pressure. I've got a new ogre of a boss about to breathe down my neck. You have my word I'll make it right with you about your car.'

'But how do I know you'll keep your word?' he drawled lazily.

'What?' Laura pulled her eyes away from her approaching boss as he passed the office next door and seemed to be heading straight for her. 'Look, just go...please. You've got my details and there's nothing more I can do right now about your precious car.'

'Ah, there you are, Laura.' Robert James walked into the room. He was a sprightly man, still handsome despite his advancing years. He smiled warmly at her. 'You've met the new managing director of James, Mr Rogan Powers?'

'No.' Laura rose from her desk and smiled at the grey-haired man who had come into the room behind him.

'Yes.' It wasn't the grey-haired man who spoke but the American stranger she had been hissing at a few seconds earlier. He stepped forward and held out his hand. 'We bumped into each other a little while ago, but we haven't yet been formally introduced,' he said with an amused smile.

Laura stared at him in shocked dismay. 'You're my new boss?'

He inclined his head. 'The ogre himself. Come to breathe down your neck with impunity.'

Her heart seemed to drop into her stomach and bounce back up again in a crazy lurch. Realising that he was still holding out his hand to her, she tried to pull herself together and limit the damage. 'Pleased to meet you, Mr Powers.' She extended her hand. 'I wish you had introduced yourself earlier.'

'I'm sure you do.' He didn't try to make her feel better—his tone was dry—but there was a gleam of amusement in his eyes as they met hers. 'By the way, everyone calls me Rogan.'

His handshake was firm, confident, as was his whole demeanour. He was very much in control of the situation. Laura felt completely out of her depth.

Her hand seemed to tingle long after he had released it from his grip. 'This is my accountant, Roland Cooper.' He indicated the man she had mistaken for him earlier.

The man smiled and nodded at her.

'Laura Taylor is one of my top interior design consultants,' Robert said with a smile. 'She knows this business inside out. A very talented woman.'

'Really.' Rogan Powers reached over to the desk and picked up some drawings she had left lying there. He leafed through them idly, yet Laura sensed that beneath the insouciant manner there was a sharp, perceptive mind at work.

He was very young to be managing director of such a large company. She wondered how he had achieved that at such a young age? Possibly Powers PLC had been a family-run company and his father and grandfather before him had built up the business.

'Have you got the photographs you took of the McClusky residence, Laura?' Robert asked now.

She nodded and got up to get her handbag from the desk behind her.

'All the soft furnishings used were from James Design, of course,' Robert continued.

She was aware that Rogan Powers was watching her, that his eyes were slipping over her slender figure and weighing her up, almost as if he could see through the fine linen material of her blue trouser suit to the silk of her underwear.

The idea made her hand a little unsteady as she closed her bag again and took the photographs out of the envelope. He took them from her and gave them a cursory look. They were interrupted by the appearance of a woman in the doorway. She was a very attractive blonde, probably a year or two older than Laura.

'Sorry, I'm a bit late, Rogan. I got held up at the office.' She also had an American accent, which was warm and almost honeyed as she spoke to Rogan.

'That's OK,' Rogan said nonchalantly. 'Karen White, meet Laura Taylor.' The two women nodded at each other. 'Karen is my private secretary.'

'These look good,' Rogan said slowly, returning his attention to the photographs, 'but, really, they don't mean a lot to me at the moment. I'm still feeling my way into the world of design.'

'Well, if you need to know anything Laura is your woman,' Robert said firmly. 'She's got a good business sense as well as an artistic eye.'

Robert was really building her up. Laura felt grateful to him, yet a little embarrassed as she met Rogan's dark eyes.

'I'll bear that in mind, Robert,' he murmured.

Laura wondered if he was being facetious. It was hard to tell just what was going on behind those dark, enigmatic eyes.

'Well, now that the team is all here, shall we adjourn upstairs?' Robert James suggested.

'By all means. Lead the way,' Rogan said easily.

One by one they filed out of Laura's office. Rogan was last. He paused in the doorway as the others walked down the corridor towards the lifts.

'I'll speak to you on Monday, Laura, about my... precious car.'

She tried not to blush. 'Yes, fine.' It was all she could think of to say.

He smiled. 'Let's hope Robert is right, and you design better than you drive.'

The door closed behind him and she flopped back into her chair, her legs feeling weak. So much for wanting to make a good impression on her new boss.

CHAPTER TWO

'ISN'T Mr Powers absolutely gorgeous?' Sandra murmured dreamily as she came into the office to put some mail on Laura's desk. 'I think I'm in love.'

Laura grinned. 'Is this the same woman who was calling him a profit-hungry ogre last week?'

'Be fair, I hadn't seen him last week.' Sandra laughed.

'He is very good-looking,' Laura had to admit.

'Mind you, Carmel in Accounts says that he has a reputation with the women—breaks their hearts.'

'With respect, Sandra, how would Carmel know that? She does tend to like gossip and she doesn't always get things right.'

'Oh, Carmel's pretty reliable. Her cousin knows someone who knows him. He's got Irish roots on his mother's side. He's thirty-seven and still single.' Sandra's eyes sparkled with excitement.

'Imagine—all that wealth and those good looks and he's unattached! Apparently he made his fortune in computers—designed games or some kind of software. He founded Powers PLC and has diversified into lots of different businesses. The company is based in New York, and they own a big department store on Fifth Avenue.'

'Really.' Laura flicked through the diary on her desk and tried not to be interested. It never ceased to amaze her how comprehensive the gossipmongering was in these offices. Someone could come in as a complete stranger and half an hour later the whole block would know their seed, creed and generation. It irritated Laura because she liked her privacy and thought it was something everyone was entitled to.

'What's this?' Laura changed the subject and pointed to her diary.

Sandra bent over to peer at it. 'Lord Fitzroy changed the time of his appointment to four this afternoon. I took the call a little while ago.'

'Oh, no!' Laura shook her head in dismay. 'That means I'll be late getting home.'

'You shouldn't be. It's just a first consultation—'

'Sandra. He's the guy with the castle—remember? I know it's about three years ago now since we did a few rooms for him, but he does stick in the memory. A one-hour consultation lasted all day.'

Sandra giggled suddenly. 'Not the one you went to with Mr James's son?'

Laura nodded. 'One and the same.'

'I do remember him now.' Sandra laughed again. 'He didn't like Paul and insisted on you doing everything.'

'Who didn't like me?'

Both women looked up as Paul James strode into the room. He was in his early thirties and a good-looking man with thick blond hair and vivid blue eyes.

'Lord Fitzroy.' Laura smiled at the horrified expression on his handsome face at the mention of that name.

'You're not going to see him again?' he asked.

'Afraid so. Four o'clock this afternoon.'

'All I can say is I'm glad I'm just a director in the company now and not a designer.' Paul sauntered over and put a playful arm around her shoulder. 'You have my deepest sympathy, Laura, darling.'

Laura laughed. 'Sympathy is no help at all. You should be coming with me. I need moral support. Or do directors not venture out into the field?' she asked playfully.

'Certainly not. They drink coffee and attend only high-level meetings,' Paul said teasingly as he patted the thick file he had put on her desk. 'I'm here in an advisory capacity only. Got a meeting with Rogan in ten

minutes. I just popped in to ask you if you'd like to go
to the cinema tomorrow?'

'I can't, Paul. My mum goes out on a Tuesday night
and I've no one to babysit,' she said briskly. She was
used to Paul asking her out. There was no romance between them—they were just good friends and very often
when one or other was without a date, or at a loose end,
they would team up and go out.

'Maybe another night, then?' Paul said easily. He
broke off as he saw Rogan Powers, strolling down the
corridor towards the office. 'Here comes the great man
himself.'

Rogan stopped by the door and looked in. 'Good
morning.' Although the tone was jovial, the eyes that
swept over them were sharply assessing. With one
glance he took in the way Paul was standing so close to
Laura and the arm which still rested lightly around her
shoulder. 'You seem deep in conversation,' he remarked.

'Trying to cheer Laura up.' Paul grinned.

Rogan sent a questioning look at Laura. His eyes were
compelling, and she felt a tremor of awareness flow
through her body. It was an effort to think straight.
Rogan Powers was far too good-looking, she thought
with panic. The dark suit sat stylishly on his broad shoulders, and his chiselled features and penetrating eyes
added up to a tremendous sexy magnetism.

Mentally Laura shook herself and switched her
thoughts to business. 'I'm to go up to Lord Fitzroy today. He's thinking of having a few rooms in the castle
restored. The problem is he has changed the time of his
appointment to four o'clock this afternoon,' she explained. 'It means I'll probably finish late.'

'Does he live far away?'

'A bit of a drive, all right—back of the Wicklow
mountains. But it's not that. He tends to take up a lot of
time.'

'He lives in a castle so I suppose he would.' Rogan's

eyes rested on Laura for a few moments. The autumn sunshine slanted through the windows and caught her hair, showing the fiery red lights in the deep mahogany strands. Her skin was very pale and soft, in total contrast to the darkness of her hair.

'In fairness to Laura, it's not the work but Fitzroy himself that takes the time,' Paul said with a laugh.

'The Wicklow mountains,' Rogan said thoughtfully, without glancing at Paul. 'Wouldn't mind a drive up there myself. I think I'll come with you.' Laura felt a tremor of unease at the suggestion. 'Come with me?' she said, trying very hard to think of some excuse why he shouldn't. 'I'll be several hours, you know. I have a lot of rooms and plans to discuss.'

'That's OK. I'll enjoy watching you in action. It will give me some idea of how you operate.'

'Fine.' She tried to sound nonchalant, as if the whole idea didn't make her as nervous as hell. What could she say? She could hardly tell her boss that she was far too attracted to him and therefore would feel safer if he just kept his distance.

His eyes flicked over her slender figure in the smart blue trouser suit. 'What time should I pick you up?'

Heavens, he made it sound like a date! 'In about two hours?'

'Fine, see you then.' Rogan glanced at Paul. 'If you are ready, we'll go over that file now.'

Paul moved to pick up the paperwork. 'I'll ring you, Laura, and we'll arrange another time for the cinema—OK?' he asked casually.

She nodded, for some reason very aware of the way Rogan was watching them and listening to them.

Sandra sighed enviously as they were left alone again. 'You lucky devil, wish I was going out for the afternoon with Rogan Powers.'

Laura didn't feel lucky, just apprehensive. Rogan Powers made her feel on edge—very aware of herself as a woman first and an employee second. It was most disconcerting.

As Sandra left to go back to her own office Laura reached for the phone to tell her mother she might be late home.

As good as his word, Rogan arrived at her office door exactly two hours later.

They strolled out into the car park together. The sky was a clear baby blue and a chill breeze was ruffling the waters of the Liffey and stirring the trees so that the red and gold leaves fluttered to the ground, where they crackled underfoot.

'Where is your BMW?' Laura asked as she noticed he was leading her to a red estate car.

'It's being resprayed today. I hired this to be going on with,' Rogan answered as he put her briefcase in the boot.

Laura was horrified. 'But you should have given me the bill or at least an estimate for my insurance company.'

He laughed. 'Laura, I decided you were right and it's just a piece of metal. Forget about it.'

She frowned. 'I don't want to forget about it. I did the damage and I should pay for it.'

'Well, we'll come to some agreement,' Rogan said offhandedly as he opened the passenger door for her.

'Some agreement?' Laura said, as he took his own seat, and frowned. She felt a bit dubious about that remark. 'What do you mean?'

He flicked her an amused look as he started the car. 'I mean I want your body in part repayment. What do you think I mean?'

Her cheeks flared with heat at the outrageously sarcastic statement. 'I don't know, otherwise I wouldn't have asked,' she muttered crossly.

'You really think I would want your body as payment

towards the respraying of my BMW?' He roared with laughter. And the more he laughed the more foolish Laura felt.

'It's not that funny,' she said. 'No, I didn't think that. I guess I'm just very independent and I didn't like feeling…under an obligation to anyone, that's all.'

He glanced across at her, taking in the vulnerable light in her wide eyes. 'I was thinking more in terms of some work that I want doing,' he said gently. 'I've just bought a house here and the lounge and some of the bedrooms could do with an overhaul. I'd very much like it if you would have a look and give me your professional opinion on what should be done. I know you are very busy at the moment but if you could fit me into any spare time you have I'd be grateful.'

'Oh… Well, I can manage that.' She smiled at him.

She had a beautiful smile, fresh, exhilarating and utterly sincere.

Every now and then there was something about Laura that took him by surprise. It was a weird sensation for just a smile, a glance, or the way she held her head captivated him.

Her dark hair was slightly wild, as if she had hurriedly tried to tame it with some expensive product before she came out but it had failed to respond totally, giving the luxuriant waves a glossy wayward bounce which was somehow tremendously endearing.

She had incredible eyes, wide and an unusual shade of green, fringed with thick, dark lashes. A guy could just sink into those green depths and be very happy, he found himself thinking.

He wanted Laura Taylor. He had known it yesterday when he had watched her in her office, her eyes flashing with anger and then dismay, every emotion so clear and vividly intense. He had been surprised at the intensity of the desire she had stirred in him. He wanted to take her to bed…wanted that right now.

He raked a hand through his hair and told himself he was being completely crazy.

Women flowed through his life. He enjoyed being with them and respected them, but the relationships were never serious. That had only happened once and once had been enough. Now he preferred to take things at a more relaxed level. For all his dalliances he had two strict rules—no married women and never mix business with pleasure.

Although Laura didn't wear a wedding ring, she did work for him. He reminded himself of this now and looked away from her. 'Better give me directions to this castle,' he told her briskly.

She leaned forward as he drove out of the car park. 'First left,' she murmured, then looked down at the notes she held on her knee. 'Then right at the next traffic lights.'

He could smell her perfume—honeysuckle and roses. It reminded him of something in his childhood.

'So, what do you think of the transition at James?' he asked.

'A bit early to say yet.' Laura was truthful. 'I have to admit everyone has been a bit apprehensive about the safety of their jobs.'

'If they are doing their work well they have nothing to worry about,' Rogan said, 'but I can understand their concerns. I shall be calling a meeting in a few weeks after I've had a chance to see the place in operation. I'll put everyone in the picture as to what to expect then.'

The steely note under his jovial tone told Laura a lot. Rogan was a businessman—a man who was probably very astute, very sharp. Certainly no pushover.

'Is that why you've come along with me today—to see how well I can do my job?' she asked directly. 'Is it a case of "Big Brother" is watching me?'

'I hope I'm not in the least like Big Brother,' he said

with some amusement. 'No, I'm just interested to see how the business runs on a day-to-day level.'

'But, nevertheless, I had better be on my best behaviour.' She smiled.

He glanced across at her for a second. 'I can't imagine you being anything other than yourself. You are very natural.'

'I'm not sure how to take that.'

'Take it as a compliment,' he said with a smile. 'I like the way you say what you think. So many people tiptoe around me in the workplace. It gets very monotonous.'

'So I can say what I like to you, then?' she asked, a mischievous light in her green eyes. 'That's a dangerous licence you are handing me. I do tend to be very forthright sometimes.'

'Now you're scaring me,' he said with a grin.

She laughed at the idea of Rogan Powers being scared of anything.

They stopped at traffic lights. 'You're very beautiful, Laura. How come you've escaped the marriage net?' he asked suddenly, looking across at her. 'You're what? Twenty-seven?'

'I'm thirty-two.' She smiled. 'Don't you know it's bad form to ask a lady her age?'

'Well, as I'm your boss, we'll call it professional interest,' he said with a teasing gleam in his dark eyes. 'Actually, I have to admit that I had all the employees' files out last night, looking for yours. I was most disappointed when I discovered that the only details I had were your name and address.'

Laura tried not to be flattered by the way he was looking at her and by that underlying husky quality to his voice. 'Robert James didn't go in much for forms and questionnaires,' she said with a shrug.

'Well, I do.' Rogan grinned. 'I did circulate some last week, but you don't appear to have filled yours in.'

Laura felt her skin grow a little hot at that. 'Haven't

I?' she said airily, knowing full well that the form in question was still in the top drawer of her desk.

'No,' Rogan said, 'so you'll have to tell me all about yourself.'

'There's not much to tell.'

The low burr of Rogan's mobile phone cut across their conversation and Rogan reached to answer it. Laura was glad of the distraction. She didn't want the conversation to drift onto personal ground.

'Hi,' he said warmly. 'How are things?' He laughed at whatever had been the reply. 'I enjoyed it, too. We must do it again some time. I'll ring you, how's that? Fine. Got to go, I'm in heavy traffic. Great. See you.' He put the phone down again.

That had to be a woman, Laura thought. She remembered the gossip Sandra had been repeating this afternoon about him being a womaniser and a heart-breaker.

It was probably true. He was single and he was attractive so he could have his pick of women. And flirting would be as natural to him as eating. She shouldn't be flattered by his manner or the way he looked at her from time to time. It would mean nothing to a man like Rogan Powers.

'So, where were we?' Rogan asked. 'Oh, yes, you were telling me why you never married.'

'I did marry,' she said quietly. 'John died four years ago in a car crash.'

'I'm sorry.' His voice changed, the light teasing quality gone.

The genuine sympathy in his dark eyes made her heart contract sharply. 'It's OK, I've come to terms with it now,' she said simply. She took a deep breath and changed the subject. 'What do you think of Dublin?'

For a moment he hesitated, then he went along with her. 'I think it's a lovely city.' They were passing Trinity College with its green railings and serene lawns.

'I live just on the outskirts, but I love it here,' Laura said honestly. 'I can't imagine living anywhere else.'

'Who's that?' Rogan pointed to a bronze statue of a woman, wheeling a barrow, at the end of Grafton Street.

'Molly Mallone, of course.' Laura laughed. 'Or, as the wags like to call her, "the tart with the cart".

Rogan laughed at that. It was a warm sound. She found herself staring at him and taking in everything about him—the fine crinkle of lines at the sides of his eyes, the sensual curve of his lips and the firm jawline that spoke of strength and determination.

He slanted a look at her and caught her watching him, and immediately she felt embarrassed.

'I suppose I'd better brief you about the client we are visiting today,' she said briskly, trying to pretend that the only thing on her mind was business.

'Maybe you'd better,' Rogan agreed, with a glint in his eye.

Did he know she was attracted to him? Laura wondered. She hoped sincerely that he didn't—it would make working with him too uncomfortable.

'What's his Lordship like?'

'A bit eccentric.' Laura started to feel better as the conversation centred on the work ahead. 'He likes to talk… I think in all honesty the poor man is a bit lonely. Although I sympathise, I feel I should warn you it might be best if we tell him we have another appointment today or we'll be stuck there for hours.'

'Got a hot date tonight, I take it?' Rogan asked with a smile.

She was about to tell him that she was rushing home to her children, but decided it was really none of his business. It was ridiculous but she was a bit nervous about mentioning the children after Sandra's crack in the office the other day. She wasn't sure what kind of man Rogan Powers was so she said instead, 'I've got plans for this evening.'

'With Paul James?'

'No, not with Paul.'

'I thought from the way he was speaking to you today that maybe you two are an item.'

'We do go out together on occasions, but it's nothing deeper than friendship.'

Rogan's eyebrows lifted at that. 'I've always maintained that it's not possible for a man and a woman to go out together and be just friends.'

'Well, we are,' Laura said firmly. 'I've known Paul for years.'

Rogan shook his head. 'I've always found that the sex issue clouds a relationship like that. Unless, of course, you have the passionate affair first—get it out of the way—then it's easier to drift into friendship.'

Laura felt her cheeks burning at those words. It was ridiculous the way he was able to embarrass her so easily. Her body reacted to him in a way that baffled her. 'I don't know how we got onto this subject,' she said with a nervous laugh, 'but I think we should leave it.'

'Why?'

'Because you are embarrassing me,' she said simply.

'Am I?' He slanted an amused look at her.

They were heading out into the country now and Laura paused to give Rogan more detailed directions on how to get to their destination, glad of the opportunity to change the subject.

The light mist which had risen as they left the city was becoming thicker the further up into the mountains they got. As they left the main roads for narrow winding ones it swirled in heavy, clammy swathes over the road ahead, making it necessary to drive very slowly.

'The castle is around here somewhere,' Laura said, her eyes straining to see through the mist. Suddenly dark wrought-iron gates loomed ahead. 'There!'

They drove through the gates and on for another few miles before the castle came into view. It was a spectacular sight, tall with round towers that soared like spears into the mist.

'Looks old,' Rogan remarked, as he parked the car near the enormous brass-studded door.

'According to Lord Fitzroy, it is reputed to have been the home of one of the Kings of Ireland. Though it looks ancient enough to be true, I sincerely doubt a lot of the tales and legends associated with it,' she said, as they left the warmth of the car.

It was bitterly cold and they stood for what felt like ages on the front step, waiting for someone to answer the bell. Then there was a sudden commotion from inside—the slither of claws on a stone floor and the deep barking of some ferocious-sounding dogs.

'Don't forget to play along with me when I tell him we have another appointment,' she reminded Rogan as she heard the bolts on the door being drawn back, 'otherwise we'll never get away.'

'Making sure you get home for that date?' Rogan enquired with an amused grin.

'Of course.'

Maybe it would be best to keep up the pretence of another man in her life so she could distance herself from him, she thought wryly. There was no need to tell him that she was rushing home to her children.

The door swung open and two Irish wolfhounds leapt out to run past them, nearly knocking Laura over in the process. Rogan reached to put an arm around her shoulders to steady her.

'Thanks,' Laura said breathlessly.

'You're welcome.' He didn't release her immediately and for a moment she found his closeness most disconcerting.

'Ah, it's you, Laura.' Lord Fitzroy's friendly voice pulled Laura from her reverie. 'Come on in. It's a terrible filthy day, isn't it?'

'Dreadful,' Laura agreed, stepping inside and shaking him by the hand. 'Good to see you again.'

It wasn't much warmer inside the hallway. The floor was slabbed stone with tapestry rugs thrown down in an attempt to stop the cold striking upwards, to little avail.

'This is my boss, Lord Fitzroy. Mr Rogan Powers.'

Rogan held out his hand and the two men shook hands.

Laura noticed how Rogan seemed to tower over Lord Fitzroy, who was slightly built, with thinning grey hair. He was dressed in an odd assortment of clothes, brown breeches, a grey jumper and a red jacket. It was as if he had just taken out the first things he'd come across in his wardrobe that morning and put them on, without looking at them.

'Just call me Fitzroy,' he said to Rogan. 'I can't be doing with all that Lord stuff. Now, come on in and we'll have a drop of the crater to get us warmed before we start.'

'Whiskey,' Laura mouthed quietly to Rogan as she saw him looking slightly puzzled.

Lord Fitzroy led the way into an enormous sitting room. There was a huge stone fireplace at one end with a roaring turf fire. Both Laura and Rogan moved towards it gratefully.

The wing chairs at either side of the fire were occupied. In one a grey cat was curled up fast asleep and in the other a large grey wolfhound was snoring.

Rogan moved the pile of magazines off the settee so he could sit next to Laura.

'No whiskey for me, thank you, Fitzroy,' Laura said quickly, as the man started to pour amber liquid into three Waterford tumblers.

'Ah, just the one to blow the cobwebs away,' he insisted, holding the glasses out to each of them.

'Your good health,' Rogan said, as he sipped the drink politely.

'*Slainte.*' Lord Fitzroy finished his with relish in one swallow and put the glass on the mantelpiece.

'I believe you want us to look at the first floor of the castle?' Laura launched straight in.

'Yes, I should have had it done when you were here last time, but even people who live in castles have to watch the pennies.' Lord Fitzroy laughed. He looked from Laura to Rogan. 'You're not the man who came last time.'

'No, I've only recently come into the company,' Rogan told him.

The man nodded. 'American,' he observed. 'That's a fine country. Met my wife there.'

Laura sipped her drink and tried not to choke on the fiery liquid. It was obviously the best Malt whiskey, but Laura didn't really drink—a glass of wine was about her limit. She put the glass on the table next to her.

Lord Fitzroy was showing Rogan a picture of his wife from the sideboard. 'That was Maeve when she was just twenty, God rest her soul.'

'She was very beautiful,' Rogan said.

'Laura has a look of her, don't you think?' Lord Fitzroy said conversationally. 'A fiery, passionate look.'

Laura cleared her throat and tried not to look at Rogan, who was studying her and then the picture. She knew he was amused by her embarrassment. 'Yes, I know what you mean,' he agreed.

'Have you any specific ideas for the first floor, Fitzroy?' she asked, hoping her skin hadn't gone too wild a shade of beetroot.

'Not really.' Fitzroy refilled his glass and went to replenish Laura's. 'You haven't touched your drink.'

'I don't drink much. I'll just sip it slowly as we work.' Laura said politely. She opened up her briefcase and pulled out a large brown envelope. 'I've brought the plans we had drawn up last time.'

'There's time enough for that.' Fitzroy waved a hand

dismissively and started to tell Rogan about the castle's history instead.

Laura stood up decisively. 'If you'll excuse me, gentlemen, I think I'll just go upstairs and take a look around. Get a feel for what needs doing.'

She left the two men talking and went to get on with her work.

When she came back some time later, her notebook filled with details of each room on the first floor, Lord Fitzroy was still talking.

He smiled at her. 'Now, you'll stay to dinner, won't you?' he said.

'Oh, no, we couldn't possibly,' Laura glanced at her watch, appalled to see how late it was getting. 'But thank you for the offer, it's very kind.'

'Oh, but you must stay. I had it planned that you would.' Fitzroy looked wounded. 'You can't come all this way, without having a bite to eat.'

'Dinner would be lovely,' Rogan said suddenly from beside her.

Laura turned to look at him, her eyes wide. She tried to remind him of their earlier agreement a note of desperation in her voice. 'But we've got another client, remember?'

'I forgot to tell you, Laura.' He shook his head, a wry gleam of amusement playing around the firm line of his lips. 'That client cancelled earlier this morning.'

When Lord Fitzroy went off gleefully to inform his housekeeper that there would be two extra for dinner. Laura looked at Rogan in agitation.

'What on earth did you say that for? Now we'll be here for hours!'

'It seemed a shame not to humour him.' Rogan shrugged. 'He's a very pleasant man. Besides,' he added, a gleam in his eye, 'I fancied having dinner with you.'

Laura tried hard not to be flattered by the way he was looking at her. 'I had other plans,' she murmured, thinking about the children. She liked to read with Matthew each night and at this rate he'd be in bed by the time she got back. 'Anyway, haven't you a girlfriend or a wife waiting?'

'No, no one,' Rogan said calmly. He reached into the pocket of his jacket, which was draped over the arm of the settee, brought out his mobile phone and handed it across to her. 'I think you should cancel your plans.'

Laura glared at him, her green eyes shimmering. It was very apparent that Rogan was used to getting exactly what he wanted. She wasn't so sure she liked his high-handed manner.

'Laura, this is a very big account and I expect my employees to give of their utmost when so much work is at stake,' he said to her in a steely tone that told her in no uncertain terms that he was the boss.

'Pulling rank now?' Laura asked with a lift of one eyebrow, but she took the phone from his outstretched hand. 'OK, you're right,' she agreed. 'It is a big account. We should stay.'

He grinned at her. 'I'll have to remember in future that pulling rank with you works.'

Laura noticed that now he'd got what he wanted the easy charm had reappeared, like the sun from behind a cloud. She hated to admit that all he had to do was look at her like that and it would be dangerously easy to give Rogan Powers anything he wanted.

'You're the boss.' She forced herself to sound businesslike and turned to go through to the hallway to phone her mother.

'Need your privacy?' Rogan remarked as she walked away from him. 'This boyfriend must be quite some guy.'

'I wouldn't bother with him if he wasn't,' she couldn't resist answering with a grin.

It was a good job that her mother was so understanding, Laura thought a few hours later when they were still seated at the end of the large banqueting table in the dining hall.

It was dark outside now, and elaborate silver candelabra lit the length of the table. A huge fire crackled in the stone grate beside them.

Cora had told her not to worry what time she got back, that she would stay overnight. Just as well, Laura thought as she listened to Lord Fitzroy, telling them about the ghost who roamed about the rooms of his castle in the early hours of the morning. It was starting to feel as if it would *be* the early hours of the morning before she got away from here, she thought dryly.

'A woman it is, all dressed in black.'

'I don't know if I believe in ghosts,' Rogan said.

'Oh, she's here all right. If you listen in the still of the night you can hear the rustle of her gown as she moves along the top corridor. She's looking for her long-lost love, the scoundrel who jilted her and broke her heart.' Fitzroy grinned. He was enjoying his guests' interest. 'Sometimes when the place is silent you can hear her sobs, echoing through the towers.'

'That's the risk you take when you make a promise to a woman,' Rogan said wryly. 'They'll haunt you, even from beyond the grave.'

Lord Fitzroy seemed to find that remark highly amusing. Laura wasn't so entertained. 'We are no longer in the Dark Ages, Rogan,' she murmured. 'These are modern times. Women aren't that bothered about getting married any more. In fact, some of them would run a mile at the very first hint of marriage.'

'Would they?' Rogan met her eyes across the table. He looked highly amused by her words.

'Yes, they would.' Maybe he was teasing her but, even so, the touch of arrogance in his voice irritated her intensely. 'It's more likely to be the women who seduce the men nowadays and leave them, sobbing in the attic.'

Rogan laughed. 'Maybe you're right,' he said slowly.

He was watching the way the candlelight flickered over her features, highlighting the bright sparkle of her eyes. It was as if the flame were burning inside Laura, a passionate, lively flame he was drawn to almost against his will.

The housekeeper opened the door. 'Phone call for you, Fitzroy,' she announced bluntly.

With a sigh Lord Fitzroy got to his feet. 'Excuse me. I won't be a minute.'

'The way he can talk he'll be at least two hours,' Laura said with a smile once they were left alone. She glanced at her watch. 'Do you think we can steer him onto the subject of work as soon as he comes back?'

'I'll see what I can do.' Rogan sat back in his chair and watched her.

Silence stretched between them. Laura glanced over and met his eyes then promptly wished she hadn't. All evening she had been acutely aware of Rogan's every glance, every smile, in her direction. Now it was just the two of them she felt unaccountably shy.

'I should be apologising for ruining your date this evening,' he said slowly.

'It doesn't really matter.' Her long slender fingers played with the stem of her wine glass.

'Good.' He smiled, a teasing, warm light in the darkness of his eyes. 'Because I'm not really sorry.'

'Work has to come first,' she said lightly, deliberately misunderstanding the husky undertone. She felt at a complete loss to know how to handle Rogan Powers. He attracted her and she knew that attraction spelt danger. She also knew he was practised in the art of seduction. She could hear the smoothness in his voice, in his eyes. She was old enough and wise enough not to be flattered...or so she kept trying to tell herself.

'I wasn't referring to work.'

'You should be,' Laura said swiftly. 'We should be concentrating very seriously on it.'

'You're right.' He smiled. It was a smile that did very strange things to Laura's pulses. 'I've been trying to tell myself that all evening. Trouble is, all I want to concentrate on is you.'

'You're very smooth, Mr Powers.'

'Rogan.' He corrected her swiftly.

'Rogan.' She assented. 'I don't think you should flirt with me. It feels wrong somehow.'

'Why?' He shrugged. 'You're not married.' Even as he spoke he was telling himself she had a point. This was against all his own rules. He'd have to stop.

'You're my boss.' She gave a small smile and from somewhere she found the humour to hide behind. 'And I'm Irish and we like to do things correctly, you know.'

He laughed at that. 'In that case, I'll try to behave myself.'

Lord Fitzroy returned to the room. 'Have you seen the weather out there?' he asked with a shake of his head. 'It's appalling.' He picked up the decanter to try and top up Rogan's glass.

'No, I'm driving, Fitzroy,' Rogan said firmly, putting his hand over the top. 'I can't have another drink.'

Lord Fitzroy pursed his lips and shook his head. 'I don't think you'll be driving anywhere, by the looks of things outside. Ah, sure, you may as well stay the night and relax. There is plenty of room here for you.'

'Oh, we couldn't possibly,' Laura said swiftly. She got up to go and look out of the window as the housekeeper came in to clear the table.

Laura pushed back the heavy curtains and was surprised to see that the fog was a lot thicker than it had been. 'We'll be all right,' she said hesitantly. 'It will be better once we hit the lower roads.'

Rogan came to stand beside her. 'I'm not so sure,' he murmured.

'Rogan!' Laura turned to look up at him, her eyes wide. 'Of course you can drive.'

'Have another drink,' Lord Fitzroy said from behind them. 'I'll go and tell the staff to make ready the accommodation.'

'That's very kind of you, Fitzroy,' Rogan said easily.

Before Laura could dissent the door closed behind the old man as he hurried to inform the staff.

Laura glared at Rogan. 'Now you are going too far. Dinner was one thing but this is ridiculous!'

'Laura, the weather is extremely bad.'

She shook her head. 'I'll drive,' she said firmly.

'Are you serious? I've seen your driving, remember?' He laughed as her eyes glittered with a fiery anger.

'No, we'd better stay. Besides, have you seen the time? It's nearly midnight—it will be four in the morning before we have all our business concluded,' Rogan decided sensibly. 'Far better to turn in, get up early and finish things with Fitzroy in the morning. His Lordship's head might be a lot clearer then, anyway. We can't, in all honesty, expect the man to sign any contracts after the amount of whiskey he's consumed.'

Laura stared at him uncertainly. What he was saying made a certain amount of sense but she felt as if she was treading in dangerous territory.

'It's up to you,' Rogan said nonchalantly. 'If you really want, we can brave the fog, just make another appointment with his Lordship and go over it all again another day.'

That swayed it. 'No, all right, we'll stay,' she muttered, then held out her hand. 'Perhaps you'd lend me your phone again.'

'Your boyfriend isn't still expecting you at this hour, is he?' Rogan frowned.

'Is it against company rules?' Laura asked, a gleam of devilment in her eyes. She was damned if she was going to tell him she was ringing her mother.

Rogan handed her the phone and watched as she went

out into the hallway once again to make her call in private.

Lord Fitzroy came back into the room. 'All fixed.' His mood was jovial. 'Una is preparing a room in the west wing.'

'That's very good of you, Fitzroy,' Rogan said absently, wondering what exactly the state of play was between Laura and this guy she kept phoning.

'All organised?' Rogan asked Laura when she returned.

'Yes, thank you.' She picked up her briefcase and started to take her files out. Thank heavens for a wonderfully supportive mother, she thought. Cora had been reading in bed and had just been amused to hear of her predicament.

'He wasn't too devastated?' Rogan asked her, a dry note to his voice.

'He'll survive,' she said briskly. 'Now, Fitzroy, would you like to look at some of these pictures?' Laura was determined that she would at least get her job done.

Lord Fitzroy filled her glass. He had been topping it up all evening, and although she had only taken a few sips from it she had lost track completely of how much she had consumed.

He peered at pictures and the samples of material for a few moments, then started to tell a story about his wife wanting to decorate their bedroom on their first anniversary.

Laura reached for her drink and finished it in one swallow. It was an instinctive reaction but a second later she wished she hadn't done it because she could feel the effects of the alcohol, invading her brain like a blanket of cotton wool.

'Maybe we should turn in for the night,' Rogan suggested soothingly, as soon as there was a lull in the conversation.

'Perhaps you are right,' she said, and started to pack

away her work. There seemed little point in continuing and she suddenly felt extremely tired.

'What about a nightcap?' Lord Fitzroy asked earnestly.

Laura shook her head, but she had to smile. She was sure, given half a word of encouragement, Lord Fitzroy would be up all night, drinking and talking.

Rogan was the first to go upstairs. 'Left-hand side of the stairs,' Fitzroy directed him. 'It's the room right at the end of the corridor.'

Rogan nodded and was going to wait for Laura but she waved him ahead. 'I'll see you in the morning,' she said. 'I'm going to see if I can get a glass of water from the kitchen.'

When she returned to the dining room Lord Fitzroy had gone. The housekeeper showed her up to her room. Laura was very grateful. She could hardly keep her eyes open and she felt a little light-headed.

She made a mental note on the way up the wide staircase to suggest to Fitzroy that he change the light fittings. It was very shadowy along the corridors and a bit eerie. The housekeeper left her outside her bedroom and went on up another flight of stars to her own quarters.

When Laura opened her door she was pleased to find there was a fire blazing in the hearth. It sent warm orange shadows flickering invitingly over a very large four-poster bed.

She didn't bother to switch any other lights on, just undressed quickly and slipped between the cool cotton sheets of the bed. Bliss, she thought dreamily.

As she drifted to sleep she was completely unaware that a few centimetres from her naked body Rogan Powers was also sleeping.

CHAPTER THREE

ROGAN turned over. The bed was warm and very comfortable. The crackle of the fire was a deeply relaxing sound. There was a scent almost like honeysuckle from the warmth of the sheets—it was deliciously familiar.

A soft sigh, barely audible yet sweetly erotic, stole through his subconscious as he lay midway between sleep and wakefulness. For a moment his lips curved in a smile.

Then he opened his eyes.

He was stunned to see Laura's face a little way from his on the same pillow. The early light of morning touched her features gently.

She looked peaceful, her long lashes sooty dark against the creamy quality of her skin. There was a faint flush to her cheeks and her lips were a rose petal shade, the soft Cupid curve full and very inviting.

He wondered if he were dreaming. How had this happened? The last thing he remembered was getting into bed and falling straight to sleep. He had been on his own then—he knew that. He hadn't been drunk. In fact, he'd managed to avoid most of the alcohol Fitzroy had been pressing on him last night. Perhaps he was still a bit jet-lagged from his flight from the States a few days ago, but he must have been in a hell of a deep sleep, he thought with agitation, as he watched Laura.

She smiled in her sleep and gently stretched the arm that was resting on the outside of the covers. The movement lifted the sheets for a moment, giving him a tantalising glimpse of breasts which were full and uptilted with perfect rosy pink nipples.

Her hand came down and rested on his shoulder.

For a second Rogan hardly dared to breathe. He was extremely aroused, and thought if she moved one fraction nearer he would have to kiss her, explore the delights of that wonderfully curvaceous body.

He was just stealing himself to do the gentlemanly thing and move away from her when she snuggled closer. Her lips were now just a breath away from his.

Then she opened her eyes.

Rogan had never seen such wide, vivid, green eyes. They were misty with sleep, like an emerald sea on a summer morning. There was a bewitching glimpse of desire for one fleeting second as her eyes focused on his. Then incredulity and shock sharply replaced it.

'What on earth…?' Laura moved back from him, her hair flowing over her naked shoulders in a wild tumble of dark curls as she propped herself up and held the sheet against her body like a battle shield. 'What the hell are you doing in my bed?'

'I was about to ask you the same question,' he drawled.

'What do you mean? What are you doing in here?' She was appalled and confused.

'I was sleeping…with you, as it's turned out.' His lips curved in a smile of total amusement. 'This has to be a first. I'm in bed with a gorgeous woman and I've hardly touched her.'

'What do you mean, "hardly"?' Her eyes widened. 'If you've laid one hand on me, Rogan Powers, so help me I'll…I'll…' Her voice trailed off in trembling fury as she searched desperately to think of something bad enough to do to him.

'You were the one who laid a hand on me, if we want to be pedantically precise,' he said, and grinned as he saw the heat rising under the pallor of her skin. 'As this is the era when women seduce men and leave them,

sobbing in attics, maybe I should be the one to be thinking of some suitable punishment for you.'

'This isn't funny.' She was as far away from him in
the bed as she could get. She noticed that she had pulled
the sheets from him so that they now rested low on his
abdomen.

He had a fabulous body, broad-shouldered with a
powerful chest covered generously in dark swirls of hair.
Before she could stop herself her eyes slipped further
down to the hard, flat stomach, and then lower. She wondered if he was wearing anything at all. The thought that
they had both been lying naked next to each other all
night made her temperature rise wildly.

'Do you like what you see?' Rogan asked with a grin.
'I know I do.'

Quickly she lay down again and glared at him from
the other pillow. 'The joke's gone far enough, Rogan. I
want you out of my bed,' she told him frostily.

'As I was here first, strictly speaking, you're in my
bed.' He made no move at all. 'You must have come to
the wrong bedroom last night...or maybe the right one,
depending on how you want to look at it.'

'If you are trying to say that I deliberately came to
your bed then you couldn't be more mistaken—or more
conceited.' She was very angry now. She would have
jumped out of the bed herself except for the fact that she
had absolutely nothing on. The knowledge made her
cling all the more tightly to the sheet.

He rolled over and leaned on his elbow to look at her,
wry humour in his dark eyes. 'Are you sure?' He whispered the words in a seductive tone.

He was too close, his mouth just inches from hers.
She found herself moistening her lips, her breathing uneven and her eyes captivated by his.

'Of course I'm sure. Look, this is all a ghastly mistake. If you would be good enough to get out of the bed

and go, I'd be very grateful.' With an effort she tried to be calm.

'Seeing as you put it so nicely.' She thought he was moving to go but, in fact, he was a little closer now. 'How grateful...enough for one kiss?'

Her heart thundered in her ears. She wanted him to kiss her. As she wrestled with this sudden awareness he leaned closer and their lips collided with a kind of wanton passion that completely wiped every thought out of her brain.

The caress of his lips against hers was sensational, erotic. She had never experienced a more explosive feeling.

For one wild moment Laura's hand moved to his chest, not to push him away but in a gesture almost of submission. The warmth of his skin and the feel of the strength of his muscles made her stomach contract with a surge of pure longing.

Rogan had intended just to kiss her and move away but when he tasted her passionate response, feeling the heat of her body as she moved closer, his good intentions deserted him completely. His hands reached and curved around her waist, drawing her nearer. She made no sound of protest—indeed, she gave a husky little moan of pleasure.

The sound ignited his passion further. His hands stroked the smooth curves of her body, finding her satin smooth, so sexy, so enticing.

His lips moved from hers to rove across her face and down the long column of her neck. Then with a groan he rolled over so that his body was suddenly pressing against hers.

Shock waves of pleasure rippled through Laura. The sensation of his body pressed so close was powerfully erotic. Heat lashed through her body. She was oblivious of everything except the bliss of his love-making, the skilled way he held her and caressed her to a fever pitch of arousal.

She felt his hands stroke the soft swell of her breasts, and felt his lips travel downwards to kiss the rosy peaks.

Her hands moved to caress his broad shoulders then up through the dark thickness of his hair. She moaned feverishly.

'Laura...?' He pulled back and looked at her with a raised eyebrow.

They stared into each other's eyes, and in the ensuing moment's silence good sense came rushing back.

Horrified by how she had just responded to him, how her naked body was pressing so close against his, she used her hand as a lever to push him away.

'What the hell are we doing?' Her voice was a whisper of anguished disbelief at how she had been so easily carried away by his caresses.

He moved away from her and sat up. He pushed a hand through his hair and gave her a slightly bemused glance. 'I think it's called making love,' he said wryly.

'I think it's called insanity.'

She was probably right, Rogan acknowledged. He certainly hadn't meant things to get so out of hand. His eyes moved to the soft curves of her figure. She was simply gorgeous.

She snatched the sheet up to cover herself, trembling with indignation. He smiled. 'The modest maiden act is very endearing,' he told her huskily. He reached out, intending to gently brush back a stray curl from her face with a tender hand, but she shrank from him as if afraid.

'Don't...don't touch me.' Her temper blazed, her green eyes burning into his.

He looked amused now. 'That's not what your lips were saying a moment ago.'

'How dare you?' she said fiercely, both to him and to the feeling he had created inside her with such nonchalant ease.

'I...I know about your reputation with the ladies, Rogan Powers. Don't think for one moment that I would be charmed or seduced by the likes of you. I'm not one of your conquests.'

He shrugged and smiled at her. 'I hate to point this out, Laura, but you wanted me. You responded to me—passionately.'

'In your dreams. You just caught me off guard, that's all.' She glared at him fiercely. 'I wasn't even properly awake.'

He laughed at that and she felt herself blushing, knowing full well that her excuses were weak in the extreme. She had enjoyed his kisses, was still very aroused by his closeness. The knowledge was very distressing.

'I'll remind you that you're my boss.' Her voice was not at all steady. 'And I expect a professional, polite distance to be maintained.'

His gaze moved to the bed between them with sardonic amusement. 'A bit late for that, don't you think?'

'We have to work together, for heaven's sake!'

'You're right. We shouldn't have allowed ourselves to get so carried away,' he agreed lazily. 'But it was only a few kisses. We are both consenting adults. I don't think it will affect our working relationship.'

It was affecting *her*, Laura thought with real panic.

'The last thing, the absolute last thing I would want would be any involvement with my boss,' she found herself babbling. 'My job is too important to me.'

'Not to mention your boyfriend,' he said calmly.

She glared at him with fury and he laughed.

'I'm glad we have the embarrassing situation in hand,' he said smoothly. 'Now, if you don't want to be shocked any further, I suggest you avert your eyes while I get up.'

He didn't wait for her to turn away and Laura had a fleeting glimpse of his strong back and lithe hips as he swung away from her before she hastily closed her eyes.

A second later she heard the sound of a shower being switched on at full blast. She glared at the door. Obviously he had just gone straight through to the *en suite* bathroom. The nerve of the man.

She sat back against the pillows, not knowing what to do.

Then she heard the shower snap off and he stepped back into the room.

Their eyes collided and he smiled nonchalantly as if they spent every morning in such an intimate way.

Rogan was only wearing a towel, strung loosely around his waist. The hair on his powerful chest glistened with droplets of water and his hair was slicked back from his face. For a second all Laura could do was look at him. He had such a fabulous body.

'Won't be a moment.' He smiled as if he was well aware of the effect he was having on her then he moved to the chair to pick up his clothes. Laura was mortified when she noticed he had to take them from beneath hers.

He flicked her a grin. 'The proof of the pudding,' he murmured, dropping her lace bra and panties on the velvet covers. 'Told you I was here first.'

He laughed as he saw the expression on her face. 'Don't worry. It will be our little secret.'

The way he lowered his voice to that husky tone made her temperature rise dramatically.

'This is ridiculous,' she said furiously. She turned on her side, away from him, hoping that turning her back on him would help to lower the tense, intimate atmosphere which had sprung between them.

He disappeared into the bathroom again, and when he returned he was fully dressed. The transformation made her heart start to thud unevenly again. He was now the smoothly handsome businessman in a dark suit, white shirt and tie.

'Don't be too long, Laura,' he said briskly as he met

her eyes. 'I've a meeting at nine-thirty at the office and we still have business to discuss with Fitzroy.'

The swift metamorphosis from teasing seducer to brisk businessman made her blink. Rogan Powers was obviously unembarrassed and unaffected by this incident. Maybe he was used to waking up with a different woman on the opposite pillow every morning!

Laura's breath escaped in a shuddering sigh of relief as he left the room. She lay there, staring up at the ceiling. She should be equally unperturbed, she told herself, but the fact remained that her heart was still racing and her body still tingled from the warmth of his caress.

Hurriedly she went through to the bathroom and turned on the water. Her eyes moved to the wash-basin. Rogan had left his watch behind, a slender gold Cartier.

Something made her pick it up. There was an inscription on the back. It read, 'All my love, Sophie.'

She put it down as if it had burnt her.

Who was Sophie? she wondered.

She tried not to think about it, and opened the bathroom cabinet instead to see what was there. She was very relieved to see some new toothbrushes, still in their Cellophane wrappings, toothpaste and scented soap.

When Laura went downstairs a little later she felt calmer and more rational about the situation. The housekeeper had made a mistake about which room she had showed her to last night. It hadn't been her fault, and it hadn't been Rogan's. Obviously neither of them had been thinking clearly this morning and it was best to forget the whole embarrassing incident.

The fog of last night had melted away into a mellow morning. Lord Fitzroy and Rogan were seated in the breakfast room. The French doors open wide onto vast sweeping lawns, allowing the dogs to amble in and out from the early misty sunshine.

Both men rose as she joined them and Rogan held a chair out for her to sit down. His arm brushed against hers as she did so and, uninvited, the memory of the way he had kissed her this morning returned with vivid intensity. Stricken, she pushed it all from her mind.

'Good morning, Fitzroy,' she said with bright, breezy cheerfulness.

'Good morning, my dear. Did you sleep well?'

Laura avoided catching Rogan's eye. 'Very well, thank you.'

'I was just telling Rogan here that I've decided to leave the decor of the rooms entirely in your hands.'

'Oh? Good.' Laura nodded and reached for the pot of tea the housekeeper had brought for her. 'I'll get my files out and we can decide what you want—'

'No, Laura. I mean I want you to decide. I was thinking of a budget of...' Lord Fitzroy pursed his lips, before naming a vast sum that made Laura nearly drop the delicate china teapot.

'Would that be all right with you?'

'Fine. But it's a very large order. Wouldn't you be happier to discuss the plans before I order the—?'

'Laura, I trust you implicitly,' Fitzroy cut across her briskly. 'You did a wonderful job last time. Just do what you think is best.'

Across the table Laura caught the gleam of laughter in Rogan's eyes. Obviously, like her, he was thinking that if Fitzroy had said this last night they could have been home early and not had to stay the night.

Laura drank her tea and tried to console herself that at least they had the order. 'I'll just have a walk around the rooms again,' she said, standing up. 'Would you like to come up with me, Fitzroy, just so I have some idea of your thoughts?'

'If I must.' The man sighed.

Fitzroy wandered through a few of the rooms with her, before getting heartily tired of the subject and wandering away.

There was no sign of Rogan or Fitzroy when Laura returned downstairs.

She noticed Rogan had left his mobile phone by her briefcase and she glanced at her watch. It was seven-thirty. The children would be just getting up. It would be an ideal time to phone and make sure everything was all right.

She was pleased when her daughter answered almost immediately. 'Hi, Mum,' Joanne said brightly. 'How are things?'

'Fine. What about you? No raving and misbehaving while I was away?' Laura asked teasingly.

'What, with Grandma?' her daughter spluttered. 'I had to go to bed at nine o'clock.'

Laura laughed. In the background she could hear the usual morning chaos of her house. Matthew was singing at the top of his voice and the radio was playing. She was filled with an absurd rush of homesickness. Completely crazy—she had only been away one night.

'Matthew wants to speak to you.' Joanne handed the phone over to her brother.

'Hi, Mum. Will you bring some sweets home with you?'

Laura laughed. 'If that's what you want.'

'I do. Can we have lemonade and chocolate tonight when you get home?'

'Sounds like our very own private party. I'll look forward to it.' Laura turned slightly and saw Rogan, leaning indolently against the open doorway, listening, and he didn't look one bit pleased.

'Listen, honey, I've got to go,' Laura said nervously. 'See you later.'

She put down the receiver and looked over at her boss.

'Boyfriend again?' he asked drolly. 'Must be a pretty heavy relationship—you're never off the phone to him. Did you tell him about last night?'

'There's nothing to tell,' Laura said crisply, trying not to blush at the remark.

'Well, you could have told him that you got what you wanted,' Rogan remarked, and then watched the tide of colour rise under her delicate skin.

'I beg your pardon?'

'I was talking about Fitzroy's contract.' He smiled. 'What did you think I meant?'

He was teasing her, she realised, enjoying her discomfiture.

'Yes, I got what I wanted. By the way, you've left your watch in the bathroom.' She decided to play him at his own game so that maybe he'd stop teasing her. 'Sophie wouldn't be too pleased that her present meant so little.'

'I've just retrieved it.' He sounded coolly indifferent to her remark and he didn't try to explain who Sophie was. None of her business, she thought.

It was half an hour before they finally set off back to town, a signed contract tucked safely in Laura's brief-case.

The sun's brief, tantalising appearance that morning had not delivered the golden day it had promised. The sky was dark, the clouds low over the country road.

There was silence for a while before Laura asked softly, 'Would you mind dropping me off at my house? I want to change, before going into the office. I'll get a taxi in.'

Rogan flicked a glance at her. 'What's the matter—want to rush home for your private party?'

'No, I want to get changed. You were listening to my phone conversation,' she said accusingly, furious at the connotation he had put on something so totally innocent.

'It was a bit hard not to,' he muttered. 'So, who were you arranging your private party with?'

'None of your business Rogan,' she said. 'Just as Sophie is none of my business.'

'Maybe we had better talk.' Rogan pulled the car to a halt by the side of the road.

'Talk about what?' she asked apprehensively.

'About what happened between us this morning,' he said calmly, turning to look at her.

It started to rain, a sudden wild squall which bent the twisted branches of the trees that lined the deserted road.

'Nothing happened so I think we should just forget about it.' She tried very hard to sound as composed and cool as he did.

He smiled. 'My grandmother…who, incidentally, was Irish…once said to me that the Irish temperament was as capricious as its climate.'

'Very profound,' Laura murmured sardonically, but she had to smile. 'But I don't know what that has to do with what happened between us this morning.'

'It has to do with the fact that this morning in bed there was a lot of passion between us. If I hadn't pulled back from you we would have made love.'

'That's not true!' Even as she denied his words she knew she was lying, but she was too scared to admit he was right.

Rain ran in rivulets down the windows of the car, obscuring the countryside in a murky mix of greys and greens and enclosing them in a cocoon, shutting out the outside world.

'It is true, Laura. I don't think we should pretend it didn't happen. There is an attraction between us and you know it.'

She closed her eyes.

'Are you in love with your boyfriend?' Rogan asked suddenly.

Laura opened her eyes and looked at him. 'That's a very nosy question.'

'I'm curious to know more about you—especially now we've spent the night together.'

Something about the deep, rasping quality of his voice

made a shiver race through her body. 'We didn't spend the night together...not in the way you make it sound.'

'We shared a bed.' He grinned across at her.

'Stop saying that,' she muttered, more disturbed than ever about the effect his words were having on her body. 'It's crazy.'

'I'll tell you what's really crazy, Laura. I'm eaten up with curiosity about your love life.'

Her heart felt as if it skipped then faltered against her chest. 'Completely crazy,' she said, but her voice wasn't entirely steady.

'I'm your boss. I'm not supposed to be interested in what you do in your free time—right?'

'Right.' Her body felt as if it were on fire suddenly.

'But I am.'

Her gaze was held by his. He had the most gorgeous eyes, she thought hazily. Deep, profoundly intense. She moistened her lips nervously.

'Rogan, we can't get involved.' She was desperately trying to be sensible, but at the back of her mind she was wondering if she was using the fact that they worked together as an excuse, a barrier to hide much deeper, more serious reasons for not getting involved with him. This man could hurt her, she could sense the danger. Her body's traitorous surrender every time he came close told her very clearly that she could lose her heart here. The last person to make her feel like this had been her husband, and John had hurt her badly. She couldn't risk her emotions like that again.

'I agree that our working relationship makes for complications. I have always had a strict rule of conduct that business and pleasure should be kept separate.'

'A rule that everyone else has to keep except you?' Laura asked lightly.

He smiled at that. 'Well, no, actually. Up until now I've always stuck to it.'

He leaned closer. Then he touched her face. The sensation of his hand against her skin set up a whole chain of reactions inside her, dulling her thoughts and fading everything except his closeness into insignificance.

She was acutely aware of everything about him in those few seconds, such as the way his eyes were flecked with a sherry brown and the faint dark shadow on the masculine strength of his jawline.

Then he lowered his head and kissed her.

His lips were skilfully seductive. They moved over hers with a tender, teasing slowness at first until she pressed herself closer and the kiss deepened. Then his lips were demanding, ravaging her mouth. She responded totally, hungry for much more.

She gave a small moan of pleasure deep in her throat as she felt his hands range down over her body, drawing her closer.

Then the only sound was the drumming of the rain on the car and the sound of their breathing. Laura wanted the moment to go on and on.

They pulled apart only when they became aware of another sound outside—that of a hooter behind them. Rogan glanced in the driving mirror. A large tractor was sitting behind them, unable to get past them on the narrow road.

'We'd better go.' He started the car again and then looked over at her. 'Will you have dinner with me tonight so we can...take this further?'

Laura's breathing felt restricted. She felt totally at a loss. 'I can't,' she said finally. Having spent one night away from the children already, she needed to spend time with them tonight.

Rogan frowned. 'We can't just leave things as they are.'

'Rogan, I think you should just give me some space to think about this.' Somehow she managed to sound calm and in control, but it was light years away from how she felt.

'If that's what you want.' He put the car in gear. 'I haven't time to drop you home, by the way.' Once more his tone was businesslike. 'I've got to get to that meeting.'

CHAPTER FOUR

LAURA leaned back and tried to relax in the silken, steaming waters of her bath. From along the corridor the sound of Joanne's music blared loudly.

'Yeah, yeah, I want you,' some rock star screamed through the house. What a day, Laura thought wearily as she closed her eyes and tried to ignore the noise.

The memory of Rogan's kiss penetrated sharply through the mists of her thoughts.

She had been out on quite a few dates since her husband's death, but it had been a long time since a man had made her feel like that. In fact, if she was totally honest she couldn't remember ever feeling so out of control—as if her mind had no hold whatsoever over her body. It scared her.

Her husband had been a charmer, smooth and wonderfully sexy. She had trusted John, loved him. It was only after his death that she had discovered that her handsome husband hadn't been all she had thought.

She shied away from those thoughts now. She wasn't going to start thinking about John. All that was behind her. She was getting on with her life. Her children, her mother, her job—they were her priorities.

She groaned and felt like sliding beneath the water as she remembered drawing up outside the office this morning in Rogan's car. They had arrived at the same time as Carmel Murphy. And that woman missed nothing.

Laura got out of the water and reached for a towel.

Now wasn't the time to dwell on the embarrassment of that scene. People at work might speculate but most likely it would die away and be forgotten.

She put on a long white towelling robe and went out into the corridor.

'Joanne, turn down that music, please,' she said, pausing for a moment at her daughter's bedroom door.

Obligingly the volume went down…but only by a few decibels.

Laura went downstairs to check on dinner. Then she put her head around the lounge door.

Matthew was playing with his game of Connects, pieces of it spread all over the coffee-table and the floor. Laura smiled to herself at the look of intense concentration on her son's face.

The shrill ring of the doorbell startled both her and him.

Captain, their red setter, sprang from his slumber by the fire to dash inquisitively into the hallway.

'Stay where you are, Matthew,' Laura said as her son started to get up. She closed the lounge door behind her and went to glance out through the window.

It was a wild night. The wind was howling around the terrace cottage, bending the trees and sending dark clouds scudding over the full moon.

As the moon came out Laura saw Rogan on the doorstep. He was wearing a long, dark overcoat and his head was bent against the wind.

She stepped back as he looked directly at the window.

What on earth was Rogan Powers doing here? she wondered in panic.

He rang the doorbell again. 'Laura, open the door. I'm freezing out here.'

With a sigh she went to the door and undid the bolts.

'What took you so long?' he said, stepping into the hall and pushing the door closed behind him.

Captain jumped up at him, his tail wagging with delight as Rogan immediately bent to pat him. 'Hello, it's nice to see you, too,' he said in a friendly tone

He straightened and looked directly at her. His eyes

moved over Laura's white robe and the way her hair was up in a ponytail. She was suddenly acutely conscious of the fact that she was in a state of undress and wasn't wearing a scrap of make-up. Still, it wasn't as bad as this morning when she had been wearing nothing at all, a little voice inside reminded her.

From above them the sound of Joanne's music boomed insistently. The sound of it increased Laura's tension. Obviously Joanne hadn't heard the doorbell, but the odds of her coming downstairs and meeting Rogan were enormously high. Either that or Matthew would come out to see who was here. It was almost a foregone conclusion that Rogan was going to meet her children. It made her heart skip and bounce.

'Getting ready for your date?' Rogan asked nonchalantly.

'I am pretty busy.' She tried desperately not to be flustered by the way he was looking at her...by that attractive husky note in his voice.

'Nice place you've got here,' he commented, looking around the hallway. The cottage was quaint and Laura had decorated it with a skill which was a credit to the James designs and her talents.

'Thank you.' She was quite proud of her home. It was small but she loved its cosy atmosphere, its warm floral chintz tones.

He smiled. 'I've come to apologise for this morning. For placing you in an embarrassing situation.'

She wasn't sure if he was talking about the bedroom or arriving at work together. 'Let's just forget about it,' she mumbled.

'Hello.' The small voice, coming from behind them, made them both turn with a start.

Matthew was standing in the doorway, watching them, an earnest expression on his face. He looked cute in his denim jeans and Aran jumper, very like Laura with the same dark hair and pale skin. He had a sprinkling of

freckles over his nose and a gleam of devilment in his
eyes.

'Who are you?' he asked Rogan with the directness
only a seven-year-old could manage, without sounding
very rude.

'Rogan Powers. I work with…Laura.' Rogan looked
from the child to Laura as if unsure of the connection.

'Oh, OK,' Matthew said easily. 'Mum, can I have my
sweets now?'

'Not until after dinner—' Her sentence was cut off by
the overhead light being switched on. Laura looked up
and saw Joanne on the staircase.

'Oh… Hi.' Joanne frowned, her eyes moving from her
mother to the tall stranger in the hall. 'I thought I could
hear voices.'

Laura felt momentarily lost for something to say.
Then she shrugged helplessly. It was just as well that
Rogan should know that she had children, she told herself sternly. 'Jo, this is my boss, Mr Powers.' Her voice
sounded high and unnatural even to her own ears.

'Really!' Joanne looked at Rogan with renewed interest.

Rogan frowned and swivelled his gaze from the jeans-
clad girl to Laura.

'This is my daughter, Joanne,' she enlightened him,
trying to sound matter-of-fact. 'And my son, Matthew.'

'Anyone want coffee?' Joanne asked with a grin as
Rogan continued to stare at Laura.

'Mr Powers is just going…' Laura's voice trailed off
as Rogan interrupted her.

'Coffee would be great,' he drawled.

'I'll go and put the kettle on,' Joanne said cheerfully,
taking Matthew's hand and disappearing into the
kitchen.

'Any more going to appear from the heavens?' Rogan
asked, looking towards the stairs.

'Any more?' Laura stared at him blankly.

'Children,' he said, a sardonic expression in his dark eyes. 'How many of them do you have hidden away?'

'Just the two, and they weren't hidden away.'

'No?' His lips twisted in a wry smile. 'Then why didn't you tell me about them?'

'You never asked.' She shrugged.

He glared at her. There was something very autocratic about him when he was annoyed...also something vaguely intimidating.

'The fact that I have children won't affect my work, Rogan,' she said succinctly. 'I am still able to give the company my undivided attention during working hours.'

He looked incredulous. 'Is that why you didn't tell me you had children—because you thought it would be detrimental to your career?'

'Well...' Laura shrugged helplessly. 'I didn't think that it would exactly help me to get on within the new company...' She trailed off as her eyes met his.

He raked an impatient hand through his hair, then lowered his voice to a husky undertone. 'How desperate are you to get on within the company? Desperate enough to come to the MD's bedroom last night? Kiss him very passionately and then bat those beautiful oh-so-innocent eyes?'

'The bedroom was a mistake!' Her skin was on fire now. 'You have no right to talk to me like that.' Her voice shook with fury. 'You were the one who initiated that...that episode in bed this morning and the...kiss in the car.'

'As I recall, you kissed me back,' Rogan reminded her, but his voice softened. He noticed the fierce gleam in her eyes, the defensive way she had angled her chin so she could meet his gaze directly. He shook his head. 'No, of course you didn't come to my room on purpose.'

The notion had been brief and fleeting. Hell, sometimes he could be so cynical. Just because one woman had ruthlessly pursued him for money and power didn't mean every woman was like that. He hated himself for the thought. Especially now as he saw the vulnerable glitter in Laura's eyes and the proud way she stood, angry yet somehow so...defenceless.

'I'm sorry,' he said gently. 'I guess I was just shocked that you hadn't mentioned your children to me. Especially as we have spent the night together.' The warm, teasing light was back in his eyes.

'We may have accidentally shared a bed, but you don't know me,' she said slowly.

'No—but I'd like to.' His eyes narrowed. 'Who did look after the children last night, anyway?'

'My mother.'

'Oh!' He smiled at her. 'You know, the fact that you have children has no bearing whatsoever on your career within the company. The only thing I'm bothered about is performance at work—nothing else.'

'I guess I knew deep down that the fear was crazy,' she admitted, 'but there have been lots of nervous rumblings since the take-over. I couldn't help feeling just a little bit apprehensive.'

His lips quirked. 'Laura, my financial director back in the States is a single mother with four children.'

'In that case, perhaps I should fill in that questionnaire you gave me tomorrow,' she said with a grin. 'Maybe I'll get a promotion. What is it, kids make bonus points?'

'You need two more to catch up with Tanya in New York.' He grinned back.

For a moment there was silence between them as their eyes met. Laura felt tension and heat escalate wildly inside her.

The atmosphere was broken by the sound of the kitchen door opening. 'Mum, there's a burning smell coming from the oven,' Joanne called urgently.

With a shriek of alarm Laura hurried to investigate. She didn't realise that Rogan had followed her until he reached to help her as she struggled to lift the deep tray of lasagne from the oven shelf.

She allowed him to take over and he set it safely on top of the stove.

They all peered at it. 'Doesn't look too bad,' Laura said. 'I think it's just caught at the edges.'

'It looks good to me,' Rogan said.

'I made you your coffee, Mr Powers,' Joanne said, lifting it up to hand it to him.

'Thanks.' Rogan grinned at her. 'And my name is Rogan.'

Laura was amused to notice Joanne's cheeks flushing faintly and the spark in her bright eyes. Heavens, she thought wryly, Rogan could even set the pulses of a twelve-year-old a-flutter.

'How old are you?' Rogan asked her in a friendly tone.

'Twelve. I'll be thirteen in a few weeks, though.'

'Your mother must have been a child bride,' Rogan remarked, slanting an amused look at Laura.

'Mum got married when she was eighteen,' Joanne informed him.

'And how old are you?' Rogan asked Matthew, who was hanging back reservedly, watching Rogan as if he hadn't made up his mind about him.

'Seven.'

'You're tall for seven,' Rogan said with a smile.

'My daddy was tall.' Matthew looked over at Laura for confirmation of this. 'Wasn't he, Mum?'

'Yes darling, he was,' Laura agreed gently.

'You must take after him,' Rogan remarked easily.

'Rogan, are you going to stay and have dinner with us?' Joanne asked suddenly, her eyes also moving to Laura—only where Matthew's were wary and uncertain Joanne's were wide and imploring.

'Maybe your mother is expecting company this evening,' Rogan said as Laura hesitated.

'No...no, I'm not expecting anyone.'

Their eyes met. 'Then, if you're inviting me, I'd love to stay,' he murmured huskily.

Immediately she could feel her pulses starting to race.

'I'll just go and get changed before I serve the meal, then.' It was an effort to sound relaxed and casual.

As soon as she was upstairs in her bedroom she started to panic about this new development. Somehow, letting Rogan stay to dinner seemed to be taking their involvement a massive step forward when she wasn't sure it was the right thing to do.

The more she was around Rogan the more she felt herself drawn to him. It was crazy, she had to work for the guy.

Laura took her hair out of the ponytail and brushed it vehemently so that it fell in long, shiny waves over her shoulders.

Then she grabbed her jeans and a jumper from the wardrobe and dressed hurriedly.

When she got back downstairs she found Rogan was serving dinner, with a little assistance from Joanne. And the table was laid.

It seemed so strange to have a man in her kitchen, organising things. She stopped in the doorway and watched for a moment before any of them noticed her presence.

Joanne was chatting to Rogan as if she had known him all her life. Rogan was now pouring Matthew a glass of Coke.

'How's that? OK?' he asked, as he only half filled the beaker.

Matthew nodded solemnly.

Laura had the strangest sensation in the pit of her stomach, as if someone had pushed her headlong into something for which she was totally unprepared. She didn't understand the mixture of emotions she was feeling. The apprehension...the longing.

'Gran comes around here every afternoon so that we won't be coming home to an empty house,' Joanne was telling him.

'You're lucky,' Rogan said. 'I used to come home to an empty house when I was your age.'

'Did your mother have to work?' Joanne asked curiously.

'My father brought me up on his own.' Rogan looked up and caught Laura watching him.

'You've managed to suss out the complexities of my kitchen, I see?' From somewhere she managed to gather her senses and walk in to join them.

'With a little help from your family.' He smiled over at her. 'If you'd like to take your seat, dinner is served.'

Laura found herself sitting opposite Rogan at the kitchen table. Joanne was still talking animatedly. In a way her conversation was a relief as it gave Laura time to sort her feelings out a little.

It seemed strange to think that this morning she had woken up with Rogan, had kissed him and now here they were, seated around the dinner table like a family. The last time her day had started and ended like that was when John had been alive.

'What part of America are you from, Rogan?' Joanne asked.

'Baltimore originally, but I have an apartment in New York now…it's convenient for business. I suppose you could say that's my base.'

'You don't live in Ireland, then?'

'I have a house here, but it's a second home.'

'Which do you prefer, Ireland or America?'

'Joanne, will you stop with the questions,' Laura said to her daughter with a smile, 'and eat some dinner.'

She glanced over at Rogan, an apologetic light in her eyes.

'I don't mind,' he said, 'but I don't know if I can

answer that last one, Jo. Both places have their own unique charm…and attractions.'

He smiled at Laura. As their eyes met she felt a shiver of awareness suddenly shoot through her. There was something about him that profoundly disturbed her senses—made her heart jump, her skin prickle with heat. She looked away from him.

'My daddy was an airline pilot,' Matthew told Rogan suddenly. 'He flew to America a lot.'

'Did he?' Rogan smiled at the boy. 'He must have been very clever to be able to fly a plane.'

'He was.' Matthew nodded. 'I'm going to be a pilot when I grow up, just like Daddy.'

'What sort of planes did he fly?' Rogan asked.

Matthew launched into a list. He knew all the names and a little bit about each.

It was a long time since Matthew had talked so much about his father. Laura listened quietly as he told Rogan that his dad had been the best in the world.

Her heart contracted painfully. John was just a shadowy memory for Matthew now, but Laura did try to keep that memory alive. She thought it was important that the children had a sense of their identity and the knowledge that their dad had loved them.

She had never once let anything slip about the problems that had existed in her marriage. The fact that John had been seeing another woman was a secret Laura had buried with him.

'He must have been a very special person,' Rogan said, listening attentively to Matthew. 'You obviously miss him a great deal.'

'Mum misses him, too,' Matthew said, looking over at his mother. 'Don't you, Mum?'

Laura smiled at her son, a great wealth of sadness in her eyes. 'Yes, Matt, we all miss Dad.'

She met Rogan's steady gaze across the table. 'How's

dinner?' she asked him, trying to lighten the suddenly tense atmosphere. 'Not too burnt, I hope.'

'It's great.' He smiled at her. 'It's a long time since I had a home-cooked meal. No doubt my sister will try to remedy that when I fly back to New York next week.'

'Are you going back on business?' Laura's heart missed a beat.

He nodded. 'Only for a couple of days.'

It was strange to feel such a sense of relief at those words. For one panicky moment she had thought he would be gone for some considerable time—she thought it best not to analyse those feelings.

The conversation moved to Joanne's favourite pop group and for a while they all relaxed and laughed. Rogan seemed to know all the latest gossip and records.

'You're very up with the music scene,' Laura remarked when finally she got up to clear the table. 'I'm very impressed. I couldn't tell you who was who these days.'

'Mum is a bit square,' Joanne told Rogan with a grin.

'Is she?' Rogan looked over at Laura. His eyes slipped over her slender figure in the tight-fitting jeans. 'She looks anything but square from where I'm sitting.'

The seductive flattery was hidden behind a teasing drawl. The children didn't notice, but Laura did.

She pretended she hadn't and pushed the last of the dishes into the dishwasher. 'OK, we'll have lemonade and sweets in the lounge before bedtime.'

Laura met Rogan's eyes over Matthew's head. 'Would you like to stay for a coffee?' she asked gently.

'Sounds wonderful.'

'Go through, then, and I'll bring the drinks.' Laura tried not to notice the warm light in his eyes. She turned briskly to put the kettle on as Joanne and Matthew went into the lounge with Rogan.

When Laura followed them with the drinks a little

while later there was a lot of laughter coming from the room.

Joanne was sitting on the floor next to the coffee-table, looking up at Rogan with intense concentration. Captain was beside her, his head resting on Rogan's knee. Matthew was sitting next to Rogan on the settee. It was a cosy scene. If she had been a stranger, looking in, she would have assumed that Rogan belonged there.

She put the tray on the table and sat opposite, listening in to the conversation for a while.

'Rogan had a dog just like Captain when he was a boy,' Matthew told her.

'Did he?' Laura's eyes lingered on the handsome face.

She liked the way he talked to her children as if they interested him, entertained him. She liked the way he was stroking Captain's head with gentle, soothing strokes.

He looked over at her.

She tried very hard to pull her thoughts away from the dangerous cliff-edge towards which they had been heading. They should talk about work, make it quite clear to the children that that was the extent of their involvement. She cleared her throat. 'We'll have to discuss what you want me to do at your house, Rogan.'

'Yes, we will, won't we?' The way he looked at her made her heart jump unevenly. It was as if he was deliberately misinterpreting what she was saying. 'You'll have to come out and have a look—perhaps tomorrow night.'

Matthew picked up his Connects to show Rogan what he had been building.

'Wow!' Rogan's eyes widened. 'Did you do this all yourself?'

Matthew nodded, looking pleased with himself, and got up to get the box so he could show it to him.

'I can't come tomorrow night. I've no one to babysit,'

Laura said. 'My mother goes out several times a week and I don't like to ask her on those nights—'

'That's OK, Laura,' Rogan broke in with a grin. 'Bring the children.'

'Yes!' Both Matthew and Joanne were quick to take up the invitation. Their eyes were shining with excitement.

'Oh, no, we can't do that,' Laura said. 'It's a school night. You've got homework.'

'Oh, Mum!' Joanne glared at her reproachfully.

'Tell you what,' Rogan said easily, 'you finish early tomorrow, Laura, and collect the children. Then you can bring them out to my house straight after school.'

'Yes, but—'

'I'll help them with their homework while you have a look at the house. And then we'll all have dinner together.'

Laura frowned, unsure. 'That's very good of you, Rogan, but I hate to impose and—'

'It's no imposition.' Rogan grinned at the children. 'But, I warn you, my cooking isn't that great.'

'Can we have sausages and chips?' Matthew asked seriously. 'That's my favourite.'

Rogan laughed and his eyes met Laura's. 'I don't think that will be a problem.'

The phone rang and Joanne jumped up to go into the hall to answer it. It was obviously one of her schoolfriends because after a moment Laura could hear her chatting and laughing with someone.

'The phone calls are always for Joanne,' Matthew told Rogan.

'Really?' Rogan smiled. 'But sometimes your mum calls to speak to you, doesn't she? She called you last night and again this morning.'

Matthew thought about that for a moment and then nodded.

Rogan looked over at Laura. 'And the party was lemonade and sweets before bedtime...?'

She shrugged. 'What can I say?' She tried to keep her voice light. 'You've found me out.'

Matthew reached to help himself to more sweets from the packet on the table. 'No more now, Matthew,' she said. 'It's time for brushing teeth and going to bed.'

'Ah, Mum! Not yet.'

'Yes, *now*.' Laura was firm. 'You have school tomorrow.'

Matthew's face fell.

'Say goodnight to Rogan,' Laura said briskly, 'and I'll be up in a moment to see you.'

Obediently the boy stood up. 'Night, Rogan.'

'Goodnight, Matthew. See you tomorrow.'

'Why did you do that?' Laura asked quietly as the door closed behind her son.

'What?'

'Invite my children to your house.'

He smiled. 'Because I wanted to.'

The lounge door opened, interrupting their conversation. 'Mum, I'm going to bed,' Joanne said cheerily. 'See you in the morning.' She smiled at Rogan. 'Bye, Rogan. See you tomorrow.'

Laura glanced at her watch as the door closed again. It was very unusual for Joanne to volunteer to go to bed, especially at the same time as Matthew.

'You have lovely children,' Rogan remarked. 'They are a credit to you. It can't have been easy, bringing them up on your own.'

'No, it hasn't, but I've had a lot of help from my mother.'

'So Joanne was telling me.' Rogan grinned. 'She lives next door, she's a widow like you and she thinks you don't go out enough.' He counted on his fingers as he reeled off the points he had been told.

Laura smiled ruefully. 'Honestly, kids! You can't have many secrets with them.'

'Some escape, I'm sure.'

'Not many.'

'Mum.' Matthew's voice drifted downstairs. 'Are you going to tuck me in?'

Laura rose and Rogan also got to his feet.

'Are you going?' She looked over at him.

'I suppose I should, but I do feel that you and I have some unfinished business.'

He moved closer to her and suddenly she felt very unsure.

'And what is that?' she whispered unsteadily.

He reached for her and took her into his arms. 'Something we started this morning.' He murmured the words gently. 'Something that has been eating away at me ever since.'

His lips touched hers, gently at first, and then as she responded he kissed her with a fierce hunger that tore into her very soul.

'Unquenched passion,' he whispered, kissing her neck then her face before finding her lips again.

Her body was out of control now and her mind knew it. Her body ached for him.

Instead, he stepped back from her.

For a moment or two their eyes met in powerful communication which left her in no doubt that he knew very well she was well and truly aroused. She tried to be sensible.

Rogan Powers was probably a master of seduction, a philanderer. A kiss—a night of passionate love-making—wouldn't cause him a second thought. It would mean nothing.

Laura's cheeks flared with colour at the mere thought of spending a night, making love with him. She tried to move away and found that her limbs wouldn't respond.

'I think it would be best if...if you just went, and we

forget this ever happened.' From somewhere she found some sanity.

'Nothing has happened—yet,' Rogan remarked, a gleam in his eyes. 'Of course, you could invite me to your room and we could remedy that.' His voice was a seductive, teasing whisper that made her skin prickle with awareness.

Laura forced herself to laugh at that remark. The fact that, in reality, there was a large part of her which was tempted by his outrageous suggestion made her feel more vulnerable than she had ever felt in her life before.

'I'll take that as a no, shall I?' he enquired with a hint of laughter.

'I think you should,' she agreed. 'For one thing, I hardly know you.'

One dark eyebrow lifted. 'What better way to remedy that?' he drawled.

She shook her head, glad that he wasn't touching her, kissing her. If he had been, she didn't think she could keep up her resolve.

'Rogan, I don't want a casual affair with you.' Her voice was clear and steady. 'I've got my children to think about. I need my job. My life is organised and I'm happy. I don't want anything to rock that stability.'

Rogan stared at her for a moment. No one had ever turned him down like that before—so coolly, so rationally. 'But you will come out to my house tomorrow for dinner?' he enquired with a good-humoured smile. 'Sausage and chips is my speciality.'

She had to laugh at that. 'Who could resist such a temptation?'

She was drawn to him against all her inner warnings. But this was just work, she told herself firmly. The fact that it made the children happy was an added bonus. It was just one outing, full stop.

CHAPTER FIVE

'ARE we nearly there, Mum?' Matthew asked impatiently from the back seat.

'Nearly,' Laura said distractedly. The narrow country road hugged the coastline, all the houses hidden from view behind trees and rich vegetation. She had to drive slowly, looking for Rogan's house.

She found the gate and turned her car up the gravel drive. It seemed to wind for ever, through trees whose leaves had turned a vivid scarlet and gold. The afternoon light was starting to fade. The last of the autumn sunshine lit everything in a rich red light as the house came into view.

Laura let out her breath in a sigh. The house was a Georgian property of considerable charm. Large and rambling, it was three stories in a warm red brick. Flame-red Virginia creeper encircled the dark green front door and the windows.

She pulled the car to a halt next to Rogan's BMW and climbed out hesitantly into the watery afternoon sunlight.

'Wow, this is fabulous,' Joanne murmured in awe. 'Do you think Rogan lives here all alone?'

'It's Mr Powers to you, Joanne,' Laura reminded her daughter gently.

'He told us to call him Rogan,' Joanne said mutinously. 'Don't you remember?'

'Yes.' Laura did remember but she was anxious to put this visit on a correct, businesslike footing. She was very nervous about bringing her children here. Why, she couldn't have said. Perhaps the fact that both Joanne and

Matthew had done nothing but rave with excitement about this outing at breakfast this morning, and again all the way here this afternoon, had something to do with it.

Or maybe it was the fact that she knew she wasn't immune to Rogan Powers—that he turned her on, excited her.

She switched her mind from those disturbing thoughts. She was here to work, to repay Rogan for the mess she had made of his car. It was as simple as that.

'I just think it would be more respectful to call him Mr Powers. He *is* my boss,' she reminded the children softly. 'And you will remember to be on your best behaviour,' she added as they walked up towards the house.

They didn't answer her, just nodded. They both looked very smart in their navy blue school uniforms. In contrast, Laura had gone home once she'd left the office this afternoon and had changed from her suit into more casual clothes—jeans and a pretty blue jumper and blazer.

Their shoes crunched on the gravel as they crossed to the front door. The air was crisp and there was a faint smell of smoke in the air as if someone was burning leaves somewhere.

'Good afternoon.'

All three of them whirled around at the sound of Rogan's voice. Laura was surprised to see that he was gardening in one of the large flower-beds that encircled the sweep of a perfectly manicured lawn.

He left the spade with which he had been digging stuck in the soil and strolled across towards them. He was wearing a faded pair of Levis and a blue denim shirt. The casual attire took her by surprise. She had only had a brief glimpse of him today in the office because he had left work very early, but as usual he had been wearing a dark business suit. Maybe, like her, he was more at home in casual clothes. He certainly looked good in them.

'Hi, Rogan.' Both children greeted him enthusiastically, forgetting Laura's words about what they should call him. Matthew even ran across to him to take his hand.

'How was school?' he asked them, ruffling Matthew's hair with an affectionate hand.

'It was OK.' Joanne wrinkled her nose and Rogan laughed.

'As good as that, eh?' He glanced across at Laura and she felt her whole system go into overdrive as their eyes met.

'Guess what, Rogan?' Matthew tugged at Rogan's hand, taking his attention from Laura.

'I've got to go to the dentist on Saturday and have a tooth out.'

'Really?' Rogan looked down at him.

'It's a baby tooth and the dentist says I might need some gas.' There was a tremor of apprehension hidden beneath Matthew's words.

'Well, that will mean that you won't feel a thing. It will be completely painless and all over when you wake up,' Rogan said gently.

'Do you think so?' Matthew asked him, his eyes wide as he sought reassurance.

'I know so,' Rogan said confidently.

Matthew grinned. 'And then the tooth fairy will come,' he said in a happier voice.

'She will, indeed.' Rogan grinned at Laura. 'Come on in and we'll have a drink.' He led the way up to the house, but instead of going in through the front door he led them around and in the kitchen door which was open.

'Would you like coffee?'

Laura dragged her eyes away from the pristine white kitchen, which was large and ultra-modern. 'That would be nice, thanks.'

'And what about you?' He turned his attention to Joanne and Matthew. 'I've got Coke, if you'd like?'

Joanne was looking out of the back window. There were some slides and a swing at the bottom of the garden. 'Can we go and explore outside for a little while?' she asked.

'I don't see why not,' Rogan said, looking enquiringly over at Laura.

She nodded. 'Don't get muddy, and don't be too long. You've got homework, remember.'

They both nodded solemnly then hurried out of the back door.

Laura smiled as she watched them race across the lawns towards the swings. 'Thanks for reassuring Matthew. He's been worrying about this trip to the dentist.'

'He'll be fine. Are you going with him?'

She nodded and turned towards him. 'How come a confirmed bachelor has a children's playground in his garden?' she asked with a laugh.

'We can thank the previous owners. This was very much a family home.' He flicked the switch on a coffee-making machine and then turned to look at her.

She was wearing that same perfume, honeysuckle and roses, he noted. Its warm tones were gentle, evoking a feeling of beauty and tranquillity.

He had been going to talk about business but for a moment he couldn't think about anything except how lovely she was. 'How was work today?'

'It was OK. I made a start on the designs for Fitzroy.'

'Good.' His eyes swept over her. She looked good in jeans. She had a fabulously curvy figure, very sexy. He found himself remembering the morning he had woken up with her...the softness of her skin, the perfect tilt of her breasts.

'You have a beautiful house.' There was a light of shyness in her eyes now, as if she had noticed how closely he was watching her and it made her self-conscious. 'It doesn't look as if it needs much doing to it.'

He made a determined effort not to think about how desirable she was. 'I like the kitchen. The problem lies in the fact that the people who owned the property before me have tried to modernise it. Fireplaces have been ripped out and newer ones put in, totally out of keeping with the character of the place. I'd like you to restore it to its former glory—that goes for the furniture and soft furnishing as well. Some of the stuff that's in here at the moment is too modern.'

'Well, I am very much a traditionalist.' She smiled.

'I noticed that when I looked around your house,' he said with a smile. 'Come on, I'll give you the tour before coffee.' He kicked off his shoes, before leading the way out into the hallway. Laura could understand why when she saw the pale-coloured carpets.

There were two reception rooms on either side of the hallway, with magnificent views down to the sea.

Everything was so neat, ornaments and flowers were positioned strategically for perfect effect. She supposed when you were a wealthy bachelor it was easy to have perfection.

He had been right. The fireplaces were wrong, as was the modern furniture.

He led the way upstairs. There were six bedrooms, most furnished basically. Rogan's room was the largest and had the most magnificent views of Dublin bay. It was a very masculine-looking room, with polished wood floors and blue rugs. The bed was enormous.

Laura didn't walk in, but stood inside the doorway, trying to concentrate in a purely professional manner. She couldn't help but notice the silver-framed photograph next to his bed. It looked as if it was a picture of two small children, but she couldn't see properly and she was loath to walk towards the bed.

It suddenly struck her that Rogan Powers might have children. Although she had been told he wasn't married, he could have a partner... She didn't really know much about him.

'Are they your children?' she asked casually, nodding in the direction of the photograph.

'Heavens, no!' They are my sister's children.' His eyes met hers. 'I suppose you could say that I'm not big in the commitment stakes.' He suddenly felt impelled to make that clear to her. As his personal battle to keep his hands off her faltered he felt he needed to make it plain that he wasn't looking for a long-term relationship.

She had two lovely children. He didn't want to hurt her—or them—so it was important to be honest with her. He also sensed a certain vulnerability in her. He couldn't quite say what exactly it was, but something about the way she looked at him sometimes with those gorgeous wide eyes brought out a tremendous feeling of protectiveness in him. It was a long time since a woman had made him feel like that.

'I have no desire to start a family at all,' he said firmly.

'Then why have you bought a family home?' As soon as the question was out she regretted it.

He seemed unconcerned. 'I wanted a base for when I'm here on business. And I think it will be a good investment.'

'I suppose it will be.' Her eyes swept around the room again. 'So, what do you want me to do in here?'

As soon as she'd asked that question she felt the colour steal up underneath her skin. Her eyes met his and he laughed.

'Now that,' he said huskily, 'is what I'd call a leading question.'

'You know what I mean.' She tried to be brisk and gloss over the moment. 'Do you want me to completely—?'

'Yes, I want you completely,' he cut across her, his tone gentle and amused. He reached out and touched her face. It was just a gentle caress but her skin seemed to ignite.

His eyes lingered for a moment on her lips.

She remembered the heat of his kisses, the need he had stirred up in her. She felt a spiral of desire curling up from the very depths of her soul, a deep yearning ache. The feeling took her body by storm and it was a shock.

She felt almost mesmerised by his eyes and his voice. The sexual chemistry between them in that instant was electric.

She dragged her eyes from his.

The children's voices drifted up to them. 'We'd better go and see what they are doing,' she said, pulling away from him.

Rogan closed the bedroom door as they left.

Joanne and Matthew had come inside and were in the lounge.

They had taken all the CDs out of the rack and were riffling through them, arguing about which one they wanted to listen to.

Laura's body had been in turmoil to start with, but this scene did little to calm her. 'I told you two to behave yourselves!'

'It's OK, Laura.' Rogan, in contrast to her, was calm and unconcerned.

He came over and bent down beside the children. 'We'll listen to these another time,' he said gently. 'Now it's time for homework.'

The argument ceased instantly and they helped him to tidy up the mess they had made.

'Sorry, Mr Powers,' Joanne said earnestly. 'We didn't mean to make a mess.'

'It's OK, Joanne.' Rogan grinned at her. 'And what's with the ''Mr Powers''? I told you, call me Rogan.'

'Mum said we should be more respectful,' Matthew chirped, 'Cos you're her boss.'

Rogan looked over at Laura with a raised eyebrow, before turning back to the children. 'I'd be happier if you would call me Rogan,' he said. 'We're friends, aren't we?'

Both children nodded.

'That's settled, then.' Rogan glanced back over at Laura.

'OK?'

The shrill ringing of the phone cut the suddenly tense silence between them. 'Excuse me.' He got to his feet and went over to the table behind them to answer it.

'This is a nice surprise.' His voice was warm. Whoever was calling was obviously somebody close to him. 'No, you didn't wake me.' He laughed. 'It's afternoon here.'

It was somebody in America, Laura concluded.

'Come on, Matthew, Jo.' She indicated that they should leave the room to give Rogan some privacy.

'I'm not exactly sure what date I'll be back in the States,' Rogan said. 'No, I won't be back then.' He laughed. 'Don't start with the dinner dates again...'

Laura was trying not to listen, trying not to wonder what he meant about dinner dates, as she shepherded the children out and closed the door.

She sat them at the kitchen table so that they could start their homework.

'Sorry about that,' Rogan said as he came through. 'That was my sister, inviting me for dinner next month.' He laughed suddenly.

'She's always trying to matchmake me with one or other of her friends. Even having the Atlantic between us doesn't deter her. She phoned to tell me she has an uneven number seated at her table and could I possibly save the day. I know what that means.' Rogan grinned at her. 'It means one of her friends is without a man.'

Laura laughed with him, feeling absurdly relieved that it hadn't been a girlfriend. 'I know how you feel. My mother used to do the same kind of thing to me.'

'Did she?' Rogan looked across at her and smiled. His warm look made her feel incredibly hot.

Matthew interrupted them with his reading book. 'Who can I read to?'

'Me,' Rogan said easily, 'while your mum takes the measurements for the house.'

It was strange how they all felt at home with Rogan, Laura thought a little while later when all the work was done and they sat around his kitchen table, eating and talking about their day. It was hard to believe that this was her high-powered boss, she thought dazedly.

She couldn't quite work him out. He was a successful businessman, a man who didn't want ties or commitments. Why was he bothering to be so nice...so good with her children? Was it just to get her into his bed? Surely not. Rogan could have his pick of women—he didn't need to go to those lengths.

He looked across and met her eyes.

Whatever it was it was working, she thought with panic. She found herself liking him more and more.

'Have you had enough to eat?' Rogan asked her.

'It was lovely, thank you.'

'Hardly exciting, though.' He grinned. 'How about us going out for Sunday lunch together? I'll treat you to something a bit better than sausages and chips.'

'That's really nice of you, Rogan, but—'

'Afterwards we can visit Mystic. I'd like to introduce the children to her.'

'Mystic?' She was intrigued.

'A racehorse I impulsively purchased a few weeks ago. She's stabled not far from here.'

'Wow, you've got a horse!' Matthew's eyes shone with excitement. 'Can we go, Mum? Please?'

'We'll see.' Laura fell back on the standby she always used when she wasn't sure about making a promise.

'Please, Mum.' Joanne said intensely.

'I've said we'll see,' Laura said gently. 'Now we should go. You've got school tomorrow and it's getting late. I think you should gather up your belongings and thank Rogan for a lovely dinner.'

Dutifully Matthew and Joanne got up. Laura also rose and started to load the dishwasher for Rogan.

'Leave that, Laura.' He came across and took one of the plates from her hand. 'I'll do it later.'

'I don't want to leave you with all this,' she said quickly. 'You were good enough to cook tea for us.'

'Laura.' He caught hold of her arm and turned her to face him. 'Leave it,' he said gently.

The kitchen door closed behind the children as they went to get their coats from the other room.

'I get the feeling you'd rather I hadn't invited you out on Sunday,' he said.

The light touch of his hand against her arm was sending a burning sensation right the way through her. 'It…it isn't that I don't want to go,' she murmured.

'So what's the problem?'

What *was* the problem? she asked herself. The children seemed to like him. She liked him. And it wasn't as if he was asking her out on a real date—this was just an invitation to the children.

'Is there someone else?' Rogan asked quietly. 'I thought when Matthew said it was them you were phoning the other night—'

'It *was* the children,' she interrupted. 'There's no one else.'

'Then why are you being so hesitant? I know you told me you don't want a casual affair, and I can respect that. Can't we go out as friends?'

'Weren't you the one who told me that men and women can't be friends?' she said with wry amusement.

'What was it you said—that the sex issue always clouds the relationship?'

'Unless you have the passionate affair first—get it out of the way.' He grinned. 'I do believe I might have uttered something to that effect. Come on, Laura, I'd really like to take you all out. And the children seem keen on the idea. It will give Matthew something to look forward to after he's had his tooth out.'

She felt herself weakening.

'I'll behave myself, I promise,' he added.

Laura smiled. 'No doubt Joanne and Matt will go on and on about wanting to go, anyway, and wear me down until I feel like the meanest monster in all the world.'

'I'll take that as a yes, shall I?' he murmured huskily.

She looked up into his dark eyes. She wanted him to kiss her, touch her—the craving was intense. 'I think you should,' she said gently.

The kitchen door opened, breaking the mood.

'Have you got everything?' She moved away from Rogan with difficulty and forced herself to speak normally as she went to help Matthew on with his coat.

'Yes.' Matthew smiled and looked over at Rogan and there was a mischievous gleam in the depths of his eyes. 'Thank you for a lovely dinner, Rogan.'

'You're welcome.' Rogan walked outside with them to their car. It was very cold now, and a light frost covered the ground. It sparkled in the bright gleam of Laura's headlights as the car turned away down the drive.

Rogan stood and watched until the taillights of Laura's car had disappeared, then he returned to the warmth of the house.

It was strange but it suddenly felt very empty. A house certainly felt like a home, with the sound of children's voices echoing through it. The notion gave rise to a hint of sadness which unsettled the confident certainties of the life he had drawn up for himself. It made him remember a time when he had dreamed of having children, and had planned them with Melony. That had been before he'd realised that the only serious thing on her mind had been his money.

Since then he had closed his mind to the idea of having a family. And it was for the best, he told himself, yet that reassurance felt extremely hollow for just a moment.

He switched off the lights in the kitchen and went through to the lounge. In the centre of the table, neatly and prominently stacked, were a pile of school books.

He went across to have a closer look. They belonged to Matthew.

Laura was in the process of tucking Matthew into bed when he mentioned he had left his books at Rogan's.

'What, all of them?' Laura was astounded.

Matthew nodded. 'Will you ring Rogan and ask him to bring them? And can you tell him that we really want to go with him on Sunday to see his horse?'

'Matthew, is this an excuse so that you can get me to phone Rogan?' Laura asked sternly.

She watched as her son's face flared a bright guilty red.

'Oh, Matt!' she groaned.

'It was Jo's idea,' he said defensively. 'She said if I left the books Rogan would bring them back and he might persuade you to change your mind about us going out together.'

'That's so naughty.' Laura shook her head. If she hadn't known Joanne was fast asleep she would have gone into her room to have words about it.

The sound of the front doorbell cut through the silence of the house.

Laura looked sternly down at her son. 'You're in trouble now.'

She left him to run down the stairs and open the door.

'Special delivery.' Rogan grinned as he stepped into the warmth of the hall and deposited the pile of books on the hall table.

'I'm really sorry,' Laura said sincerely. 'I can't believe that he did that.'

'Well, it's easy to forget things. Good job I don't live too far away.'

'Mum, is that Rogan?' Matthew called downstairs anxiously. Can I see him? I want to tell him something.'

'Go to sleep,' Laura called back.

Humour gleamed in Rogan's eyes.

'You know he did this on purpose,' Laura said in a low tone. 'It was a ploy to get you out here so you could talk me into going out with you on Sunday.'

Rogan laughed. 'Didn't you tell him I had already done that?'

'No… I'm wondering if as a punishment for this I should tell him we're not going,' she said.

'Who are you trying to punish—the children or me?' Rogan enquired drolly. 'Don't do that, Laura.' Her heart seemed to skip crazily at those words.

'Mum,' Matthew called again.

'Let's see what he wants,' Rogan said with a smile.

Laura found herself leading the way upstairs. Her son's room was directly opposite her own. The door was open and he was in bed.

Rogan smiled as his eyes moved over the child in his red pyjamas, his teddy bear snuggled close to him on the pillow.

'What is it, Matt?' he asked gently.

'I just wanted to say sorry.'

'I should think so.' Laura moved to tuck the blankets around him more securely.

Matthew looked over towards Rogan, who was standing at the foot of his bed. 'Can we still come and see your horse?' he asked, his eyes wide and questioning.

'You can,' Rogan agreed cheerfully.

His eyes flicked around the room and took in the model aeroplanes that hung from the ceiling and the framed photograph of a man in his pilot's uniform beside the bed, before resting for a moment on the tender way Laura brushed back a stray lock of dark hair from the child's forehead.

'Now get some sleep.' Laura pressed a kiss against the child's cheek, before turning off the lamp. 'Goodnight, Matthew.'

'Night, Mum. Night, Rogan.'

As they closed the door on him, Rogan smiled at her. 'He seems happy now, anyway.'

'Now he's got his own way, you mean?' Laura grinned.

'He's a true man in the making,' Rogan agreed with an indulgent gleam in his eye.

He looked across the corridor towards Laura's bedroom. The door was open and the bedside lamp was on. It sent a soft light over the white daisy covers on the bed, then caught the jewellery that sat on a stand on the pine dressing-table.

'Do you have a photograph of your late husband beside your bed?' Rogan asked her suddenly.

The question took her by surprise. 'No... I put that away a long time ago,' she answered hesitantly.

Their eyes met and Laura could hear her heart beating wildly in the silence between them. She made to turn away from him but he reached out and pulled her gently towards him.

'I've been wanting to kiss you all evening,' he said in a low velvety tone.

She found herself staring up at him with a feeling of helplessness. She wanted him to kiss her. He touched his fingers against her lips. The feeling was erotic.

'I'd like to take you to bed and kiss every little part of you.' His voice was so low that she could barely hear him.

She couldn't speak, could hardly think.

He moved closer and his lips touched where his fingers had rested, carefully caressing the warmth of her lips.

She responded, kissing him with a passion that was suddenly wild and demanding. Maybe she could handle an affair, her body cried out. His hands touched her, lightly caressing, not assertive, just gentle, tender… exquisitely tormenting.

'I should go.' He was the one to move back from her. 'If I don't I'm going to want to take this further.' He reached out and touched her face. 'Much further.'

Laura watched him walk away from her down the stairs and it took all her strength not to call out for him to come back. He stopped at the foot and looked up at her.

'What are you doing Thursday night?' he asked suddenly.

'Thursday?' Laura hesitated, surprised by the question.

'I don't want to wait until Sunday, before seeing you again socially.'

The husky admission made Laura's mind fly into a whirl of confusion. 'It's Hallowe'en,' she recalled. 'The children are both going out to parties. Matthew is sleeping over at his friend's house.'

'I wasn't inviting the children,' Rogan said smoothly, 'just you. I'd like to take you to dinner.'

'Oh.' She looked down at him and her heart seemed to beat so loudly that it was like a drum, beating overtime.

'How about it?'

She smiled, her resistance melting. 'I'll look forward to it.'

CHAPTER SIX

THE house was unusually silent, so quiet, in fact, that the sound of the clock in the hall seemed far too loud. Its ticking reminded Laura that Rogan's arrival was imminent.

A couple of hours ago the house had been in chaos as Matthew and Joanne had raced around, getting ready for their fancy-dress parties. There had been a good deal of laughter and frivolity and it had helped to take Laura's mind off the fact that tonight it would just be her and Rogan.

Now she stood before the mirror in a plain black jersey dress and tried to stifle the butterflies which seemed to have emerged from nowhere.

She hadn't spoken to Rogan on a personal level since the other night when he'd brought back Matthew's books, but today in the office his eyes had caught hers and the feeling of sexual magnetism had been so overpowering that Laura had felt weak. Just remembering the throbbing sensation of heat made her heart thump unevenly in her chest.

This was definitely a mistake. She was too attracted to him.

The sound of the doorbell made her whole body go into a state of alarm. She glanced at her reflection and tried to reassure herself. It was just a date, she would keep him at arm's length and they would probably spend the evening talking about work.

The reassurance she gained from telling herself this flew out of her mind once she had opened the front door to him. Rogan was wearing a dark suit and a black cashmere overcoat which seemed to emphasise the power of his build and the darkness of his hair and eyes. He looked spectacular.

'Hi.' He smiled at her, a smile that tied her emotions into knots.

'Hi.' It was all she could think of to say. She stepped back and allowed him to enter.

'You look nice,' he said nonchalantly, yet the male gleam of appreciation in the darkness of his eyes was anything but casual.

'Thank you.' She reached for her coat and tried to ignore the flutter of awareness that accompanied just the merest brush of his fingers as he helped her to put it on.

'Listen, I—'

'I thought—'

They both started to speak at the same time.

'You first.' He grinned at her.

She found herself grinning back at him. She said with a husky honesty, 'This is kind of crazy, isn't it? I don't know about you, but I feel very unsure about us, going out together on a date.'

One eyebrow lifted at that, but before he could say anything she rushed on. 'You said yourself that you have a strict rule against mixing business with pleasure. I can't help feeling that it is a very sensible rule.'

'It is,' he agreed softly, then he reached to touch her face. 'But I don't seem to be able to play by the rules where you are concerned. Believe me, I've been trying to.'

The caress of his fingers made her heart almost stop, then jerk crazily into double time. She had to force herself to move back from him.

'Perhaps we should try a bit harder,' she said, her voice not entirely steady. 'I meant what I said about not wanting complications in my life, Rogan. I…I just want to make it clear to you that I haven't changed my mind.

I'm having dinner with you tonight as a friend... It isn't anything deeper.'

'I won't get my hopes up, then,' he said. There was a mischievous glint in his eye as he spoke, one which made her laugh.

'I'm sorry. I'm rambling on needlessly, aren't I?' She shrugged. 'You were probably thinking the same thing.'

'In theory, maybe,' he admitted with a grin. 'You'll have to help me out and slap me back if I get out of control.'

She smiled at the light-hearted words, but deep down she knew that she, too, had difficulty in keeping control of her senses around him.

The night air was laced with the smoke from bonfires, which hung, like a stage effect, around the glow of the streetlights. Three children dressed as witches darted across the gateway with their cloaks flying out behind them, the fleeting snatch of their laughter the only sound on the quiet road.

'There is some black magic cooking tonight, by the sound of it,' Rogan said with some amusement. 'What did Joanne and Matthew dress up as?'

Laura smiled. 'Matthew is Spiderman and Joanne is a black cat. We had fun getting the make-up and the clothes just right, I can tell you.'

'I bet you did.' Rogan laughed. He unlocked the car. 'Bearing in mind that you have to be home for when Joanne gets in, I booked a table at a local restaurant.'

'Oh... That was thoughtful of you.' Laura hesitated. She remembered she had told him that Matthew was sleeping over at his friend's house tonight, but since then Joanne's plans had changed and she had also arranged to sleep over with a friend.

For some reason she shied away from enlightening him that she had the house to herself tonight, instead changing the subject. 'So, which restaurant did you book?'

'Shelley's.'

'Heavens!' Laura's eyebrows rose slightly. He had chosen one of the trendiest, most expensive of restaurants.

'What's the matter? Is the food no good?'

'I don't know, I've never eaten there. Apparently, the prices are out of this world.'

'Let's hope the food is as well,' Rogan said.

The food was excellent, as was the ambience of their surroundings. Polished wood floors reflected the glow of candlelight, and the tables were set in secluded wooden booths so that diners had maximum privacy.

Laura really enjoyed the evening, but most of all she enjoyed Rogan's company. He was an amusing and fascinating man. They were halfway through their main course when it dawned on her that they hadn't discussed work once and that she didn't want to.

'What's it like, living in Manhattan?' she asked as he leaned over to pour her a glass of wine.

'Well, people tend to live life at full speed. They don't just have one business lunch—they have two within the hour.'

Laura laughed. 'At least there's no time to get bored.'

'No time for anything.' He poured himself a mineral water. 'I spend my days running between meetings and deals.'

'You must enjoy it, otherwise you wouldn't do it, would you?'

'Once you get on the treadmill it's hard to get off.' He smiled. 'But, yes, I suppose I still get a kick out of a successful deal.'

'You sound as if business takes up much of your life.'

'It does,' he acknowledged. 'I suppose it's a price you pay if you want to be successful. Relationships seem to have taken a back seat.'

'Even Sophie?' She tried to sound casual as she asked him that question but, in fact, she had been eaten up with curiosity about who Sophie was since she'd read the inscription on his watch.

'Sophie is very much past history,' he said firmly.

When he didn't enlighten her any further she just shrugged and said lightly, 'Well, it's no wonder you aren't looking for heavy relationships. It seems Powers PLC is a demanding mistress.'

'Not exactly.' He smiled. 'There is still room in my life for a demanding mistress.' His eyes met and held hers across the table. She felt her skin tingle with an awareness of him which was purely sexual.

'I've embarrassed you now.'

'No. I know you are only joking.' She hoped her skin wasn't as hot-looking as it felt.

'Am I?' he murmured softly. 'To be honest with you, Laura, it isn't my work that holds me back from having a serious relationship with a woman. I've seen too many marriages crumbling around me, my own parents' marriage amongst them. Nowadays, I feel an allergic reaction coming on whenever anyone even mentions the word 'commitment.''

Although there was a gleam of humour in his eyes she sensed that beneath it he was very serious.

'How old were you when your parents split up?' she asked curiously.

'Ten. It was a very unhappy period of my life. My parents argued like crazy and then one day, out of the blue, my mother left. She took my sister with her...oh, and the dog.' He smiled, a mocking kind of smile. 'She left me with my father because she said it would be cruel to leave Dad all alone and us ''men'' would be good company for each other.'

Laura stared at him, saddened by the story, her heart going out to him. 'How awful for you.'

'I adjusted, and my father was a good man.' He shook his head. 'I don't know why I just told you that.' He sounded uncomfortable. 'It's years since I talked about my parents' divorce.'

'I'm glad you told me,' she said softly.

Their eyes met and held for a few moments before she looked away, confused by the emotions he stirred up in her.

'It makes me realise you are not quite the tough guy you pretend to be.' She tried to lighten her tone to break the feeling of intimacy. 'And I don't blame you for being wary of marriage,' she said candidly. 'It's not for the faint-hearted.'

He frowned. 'But it's not all like that. You were happy, weren't you?'

She hesitated, her mind dissecting his question. She had been happy, but she had been living a lie. John hadn't loved her. 'Yes, I was happy.' Some things were too painful to discuss, she decided.

His eyes moved over her, noting the sudden shadows in the vivid green eyes. 'But you're afraid of being hurt again,' he suggested gently.

'What makes you think that?' She was taken aback by his perception. He was right—she was afraid of opening her heart, of being betrayed and hurt again. But how could he possibly know?

He smiled. 'I can see it in your eyes. You have a vulnerable, almost "little girl lost" look about you sometimes.'

'And I hoped I looked like a confident career-woman.' She had been startled by his observation. It made her feel exposed, as if her protective barriers had been ripped away, leaving her wide open to him.

'You do.' He nodded. 'Just every now and then I catch a glimpse of what is beneath.' He reached out and covered her hand with his.

The warmth of his touch did very strange things to Laura's emotions. She felt as if he had brought her to the edge of some precipice and now she was holding onto her balance by a thread. She forced herself to pull her hand from his.

'Have there been any serious relationships in your life since your husband died?' Rogan asked suddenly.

'I've been out on some dates,' Laura answered hesitantly, 'but I've got to be careful. I've got the children to consider. They have to come first.'

Rogan nodded. 'And I suppose the pain of losing someone you loved must be very hard to get over,' he said gently.

He thought her reluctance to get involved with a man again was due to grief. It was something of a relief to know he hadn't guessed how much more complex her feelings were. The shock of her husband's infidelity had torn away her confidence. She found it hard to trust men now.

The waiter interrupted them, and Rogan asked if she would like dessert and coffee.

'Nothing more for me, thank you. It was a lovely meal,' Laura said sincerely.

As they were left alone again Laura's eyes moved thoughtfully over Rogan's handsome features. He was very suave and sophisticated yet she had seen another side of him tonight. Behind that veneer there was a gentleness, a warmth, that made Laura like him all the more. 'You're welcome to come back to my house for coffee,' she offered impulsively.

'That would be nice.' He smiled confidently, a smile that told her Rogan was well used to melting woman's hearts. She wondered if inviting him back had been a mistake.

It seemed colder than ever outside. There was a freezing fog and the road surfaces were slick and icy. It was a relief to get into the car and turn on the engine.

'How's Joanne getting home?' Rogan asked as he swung the car out of the car park. 'Would you like me to pick her up on the way?'

His concern for her daughter touched her. 'No, thanks, Rogan, there's no need. She decided she wanted to sleep over at her friend's house.'

'Really?' He said no more until he had negotiated the traffic and was pulling into her road. 'So you've got the place to yourself tonight.'

'Yes, very unusual.' Her jovial reply was tinged with uncertainty. The butterflies were back.

He pulled the car to a halt by her front door and they hurried in from the cold.

The house was still warm from the central heating but Laura asked Rogan if he wouldn't mind lighting the fire while she made the coffee.

When she returned to the lounge with their drinks the turf fire was blazing and Captain had moved himself from his slumber by the radiator to lie in front of it.

'That's the life, isn't it?' Laura said with a smile as she looked with affection at the sleeping dog.

She sat on the settee next to Rogan and reached to pour his coffee. The soft crackle of the fire was the only sound in the house.

The silence between them lengthened. It wasn't an uncomfortable silence but it was loaded with tension, a sensual tension which had been increasing all night every time their eyes met, every time he brushed against her. The knowledge that they were sexually attracted to each other lay like a trap, waiting to be sprung, waiting to compromise both of them. It was too dangerous an attraction to acknowledge.

'I've got a meeting with the design team tomorrow to discuss the renovations for the castle.' She resorted to work in an attempt to lighten the atmosphere. 'I've put some preliminary ideas on the computer already and—'

'Laura.' He cut across her. 'Let's talk about that to-morrow.' His voice was firm, as was the hand that reached out, took the coffee-cup from her and placed it back on the table. 'Work belongs in the office,' he said huskily.

'I…I thought we had agreed we were playing things by the rules…' Her voice trailed off as he reached out to touch a strand of her hair with a tender, stroking caress.

'I know what we said.' His lips slanted in a self-derisory smile. 'Believe me, I keep kicking myself, trying to remind myself of it, but I'm fighting a losing battle because I just can't resist you.'

His lips were inches from hers. If she swayed against him she would be in his arms. The temptation was overwhelming.

'You know I read…somewhere…that some firms in America have outlawed office romances.' She tried desperately to think straight. 'Apparently, they are bad for production.'

'Really?' Rogan's lips curved in a mischievous grin. 'Well, I think that's a mistake. I've come to the conclusion that nothing is more enticing than forbidden fruit.'

His lips touched hers. The sensation was overwhelmingly sensual. His caress was gentle, yet had all the power of a hurricane on her senses. She put one hand on his shoulder and he moved closer and kissed her again.

'This is probably a big mistake,' she murmured, but her words were fevered with passion.

'A big mistake,' he echoed. His hand moved to hold her close against his body.

Laura held onto him tightly, loving the feel of his caresses. She revelled in them, lapping them up, greedy for so much more.

For a long while they just kissed, the softness of his lips and the wildness of his passion setting Laura's body on fire. She felt his hands on the zip at the back of her dress and she didn't try to stop him as he gently slipped it down. She wanted the touch of his hands against her skin.

She was wearing a black lacy bra under her dress, and he stroked the lace aside and kissed her breast with an unreserved hunger that made her groan with pleasure.

Laura pressed herself closer to him. The soft material of his suit against her naked skin felt incredibly erotic.

'Laura, I want to make love to you.' He whispered the words against her ear in a low husky tone.

The demanding yet sensual note in his voice made her emotions boil.

'I don't know, Rogan. I'm not sure.' Her voice came out in a rush of panic as his hand moved to the buckle on the belt of his trousers.

He stopped and looked at her. 'Hell, maybe you're right.' He pushed a hand through his hair, as if willing himself to get his thoughts in order and his passion back under control.

He looked down at her, noting the way she was now holding her dress in front of her body in a defensive way.

'I think I should go,' he said quickly.

'Yes.' It took all her control to agree with him. He stood and reached for his coat. Then quietly, without another word—without even looking back at her—he let himself out of the front door.

For a while Rogan sat in his car. Even the cold night air didn't help to cool his ardour, but he was glad he had pulled back from her. She seemed too vulnerable for a casual affair and it was all he could offer.

He needed to call a stop to this, he told himself firmly.

CHAPTER SEVEN

LAURA stared unseeingly at the work in front of her. All that played in front of her eyes was the scene on her settee last night. Over and over it went, mocking her, tormenting her.

She had wanted Rogan so badly. The thought of lying upstairs in her bed with him had been a temptation her body had craved.

Her office door opened and her nerves jangled violently as for a second she thought it might be Rogan. She didn't know if she was relieved or disappointed when she looked up to find that it was her secretary.

'I'm collecting for Robert James's leaving present.' Sandra waved a large jar in Laura's direction.

'What are we buying him?' Laura reached to get her purse.

'Some Waterford crystal. We'll present it at the leaving party next week.'

Laura pushed a note into the jar.

'It should be a really good party, you know. Rogan is helping to organise it.'

'Is he?' Laura was surprised.

'He's such a nice guy.' Sandra sighed dreamily. 'I'm just hoping that he will have one dance with me.'

Did the whole world have a crush on Rogan Powers? Laura wondered dryly.

'By the way, Shay O'Leary has been on the phone,' Sandra went on in a more serious tone. 'He has the fireplaces you ordered for Rogan's house and he can deliver tonight after six.'

Laura nodded. 'Have you checked the time is OK?'

'No. Rogan's been in a meeting all morning. I told Shay we'd phone him back and confirm.'

The knowledge that Rogan had been tied up all morning was vaguely reassuring. At least he hadn't been deliberately avoiding her.

Sandra glanced at her watch. 'I'll check with his secretary now. He should be finished.'

'No. Don't bother.' Laura said impulsively. 'I'll go up and see him. There are a few details I want to discuss about his house, anyway.'

It was an ideal excuse, she told herself as she reached to get his file. She desperately wanted to know how he felt about the way things had gone between them last night, and it was better to do it under the guise of work—see how he reacted to her.

As the lift doors closed and whisked her smoothly to the top floor Laura felt her heart pounding with anticipation. The thought of being alone with Rogan for even five minutes acted on her like an aphrodisiac.

Was she out of her mind? she berated herself sharply.

Wasn't it crazy in the extreme to lower her defences around a man who seemed irresistible to women? She really had to get a grip.

The lift doors swished open and she walked slowly towards his office.

She'd go in there and tell him that last night had been a mistake and would never be repeated, she told herself sternly. Then she found herself wondering if Rogan would say the same thing to her.

Rogan's secretary, Karen White, looked up as she entered the room.

'I'd like to speak to Mr Powers for a few minutes, if I may?' Laura requested politely.

The woman pursed her lips and shook her head. 'Have you an appointment?'

'No—'

'Then, I'm sorry, you can't see him.'

At that moment the door to the inner office opened and Rogan came out with another man. 'Thanks, Len, I'll look into it before the next meeting,' Rogan said in a friendly tone.

He glanced over towards Laura as the man left. 'Hello, Laura,' he said. 'What can I do for you?'

Although his tone was businesslike, she noticed the way his gaze lingered for a fraction of a second on her long legs and shapely figure. She was glad she had worn her pale vanilla suit. She knew she looked good in it and she needed the boost to her confidence.

All her sensible thoughts seemed to be deserting her. All she could think about was how wonderful it had felt to be in Rogan's arms.

'Just wanted to have a word about the decor for your house.' Somehow she managed to sound brisk.

He smiled and she wondered if he realised that she was just using an excuse to see him.

'OK, give me a moment. I've got to make a phone call first. Take a seat.' He indicated the comfortable seats behind her.

'If you are too busy it doesn't matter,' she said quickly. 'I've got an appointment in a little while, anyway...'

'Laura, it's fine. I won't be long.' He returned to his office and the door closed.

Laura met Karen's cool, glittering gaze. She had the distinct impression that the attractive secretary did not like her or the fact that she was to be granted an appointment when she had turned Laura away.

Karen returned her attention to her keyboard. The sound of her fingers hitting the keys punctuated the frosty atmosphere.

Laura sat. Her eyes moved from the secretary to the pictures on the walls. Some were of the New York office and some of what looked like a large department store.

PLAY "LUCKY 7"
AND GET AS MANY AS 5 FREE GIFTS...

HOW TO PLAY:

1 With a coin, carefully scratch away the silver panel opposite. Then check the claim chart to see what we have for you – FREE BOOKS & GIFTS – ALL YOURS! ALL FREE!

2 Send back this card and you'll receive specially selected Mills & Boon novels from the Presents™ series. These books are yours to keep absolutely FREE.

3 There's no catch. You're under no obligation to buy anything. We charge nothing for your first shipment. And you don't have to make any minimum number of purchases – not even one!

4 The fact is thousands of readers enjoy receiving books by mail from the Reader Service™. They like the convenience of home delivery and they like getting the best new romance novels at least a month before they are available in the shops. And of course postage and packing is completely FREE!

5 We hope that after receiving your free books you'll want to remain a subscriber. But the choice is yours – to continue or cancel, any time at all! So why not take up our invitation, with no risk of any kind. You'll be glad you did!

We all love mysteries… so as well as your free books, there may also be an intriguing gift waiting for you! Simply scratch away the silver panel and check the claim chart to see what you can receive.

Play

"Lucky 7"

P8KI

Just scratch away the silver panel with a coin. Then check below to see how many FREE GIFTS will be yours.

YES! I have scratched away the silver panel. Please send me all the gifts for which I qualify. I understand that I am under no obligation to purchase any books, as explained on the opposite page. I am over 18 years of age.

MRS/MS/MISS/MR _____ INITIALS _____

BLOCK CAPITALS PLEASE

SURNAME _____

ADDRESS _____

_____

POSTCODE _____

► DETACH AND RETURN THIS CARD TODAY. NO STAMP NEEDED! ►

THE READER SERVICE: HERE'S HOW IT WORKS

Accepting free books places you under no obligation to buy anything. You may keep the books and gift and return the despatch note marked "cancel". If we don't hear from you, about a month later we will send you 6 brand new books and invoice you for just £2.30* each. That's the complete price – there is no extra charge for postage and packing. You may cancel at any time, otherwise every month we'll send you 6 more books, which you may either purchase or return – the choice is yours.

*Terms and prices subject to change without notice.

THE READER SERVICE™
FREEPOST SEA3794
CROYDON
Surrey
CR9 3AQ

If offer card is missing, write to: The Reader Service, P.O. Box 236, Croydon, Surrey CR9 3RU.

The phone rang on Karen's desk and she snatched it up.

'Rogan Powers's office. Hold the line one moment, please,' she said in a lilting tone, before flicking the switch on the intercom. 'Rogan, sorry to interrupt but your wife is on line two. Do you want me to put her through? OK, will do.'

The shock was immense. For a moment Laura wondered if she had misheard. Rogan Powers—married?

'Yes, Mrs Powers, putting you through in one moment,' Karen was saying smoothly.

Laura hadn't misheard.

The lies, the deceit, made Laura feel sick as for one awful moment memories of her own husband's infidelity came flooding back.

She rose and Karen looked over at her.

'It sounds like Rogan will be a while,' she said quickly. 'Tell him I'll speak to him later.'

Was that her voice—so cool, so controlled? Inside she felt like hitting Rogan, fiercely smacking that smugly handsome face.

She didn't remember getting back to her office. She sat behind her desk, fizzing with fury—and with pain.

How could she have been so taken in? Allowed herself to believe his lies? All that talk about being frightened of commitment... Hell, he had even evoked tenderness and empathy within her when he had spoken of his parents' divorce. He had seemed so genuine.

And all along he had been cheating on his wife.

Her office door opened and she looked up as Robert's stepson, Paul, came in.

'Hello, gorgeous, how are things?' He grinned at her in his usual good-natured, teasing way.

'Not so bad.' With a supreme effort Laura forced herself to sound relaxed. 'What are you doing here?'

'Meeting with Rogan Powers,' he said. 'I tried to ring you on Tuesday night but there was no answer. I thought you said you couldn't go out because you'd no one to babysit?'

'I took the children out for something to eat.' The memory of that trip to Rogan's house taunted her. That wonderful way he had with her children. Maybe he had children of his own—if he'd lied about one thing he could lie about the other. Hurriedly she put a stop to those thoughts.

'Sorry, Paul, was there something in particular you wanted?' She focused her attention on him with difficulty.

'I was wondering if you'd like to accompany me to this party for Robert next week.'

Laura hesitated.

'Oh, go on, Laura. Say you'll come with me. It will make my night.'

Laura glanced up and saw Rogan Powers, walking down the corridor towards her office. She felt a frisson of absolute loathing for him. He looked sensational in his dark suit, his tall, well-built body drawing female eyes to him the way flowers attracted butterflies.

'So, what do you say, have we got a date?' Paul pulled her attention away from her boss.

'Yes, Paul. It's a date,' she found herself saying firmly.

'Great!'

The door of the office opened and Rogan strolled in. Paul smiled a greeting at the other man. 'Hello, Rogan, good to see you.'

The two men shook hands. 'I was a few minutes early for our appointment so I thought I'd have a few words with Laura.'

Rogan's eyes moved over towards her. 'I wanted a few words myself,' he drawled. 'Perhaps you'd go on up to my office, Paul. I won't be a moment.'

'Fine.' Paul smiled at Laura. 'I'll ring you later.'

She nodded.

'What was all that about?' Rogan asked as the door closed behind the other man.

'It was personal.' Laura was so mad with him she couldn't bring herself to look him in the eye.

There was a brief pause and she could feel the tension coiling between them.

John had cheated on her, lied to her. Rogan was doing the same to his wife and she wouldn't be a part of it.

She suddenly remembered the outing they had arranged for Sunday. Of course, that was now out of the question. The knowledge that Joanne and Matthew would be bitterly disappointed added to her fury.

'It certainly looked personal,' Rogan remarked calmly, 'but you're right. It's none of my business.'

She looked up at him and her eyes shimmered a vivid intense green.

'You rushed off, without seeing me. I wondered why,' he said nonchalantly.

'I didn't have time to wait around for you.' Her voice was overly bright as she tried to force herself to concentrate on business. 'I only wanted to know if there would be anyone in your house after six. I've found the correct Georgian fireplace for you and the guy wants to deliver.'

He shook his head. 'I won't be home until late. Can you reschedule, perhaps for tomorrow morning?'

'Yes, I'll do it now,' she murmured, raking through her files in an efficient way to find the phone number. She didn't dare to look at Rogan again or say anything personal because she was only just holding onto her temper. If she told him what she thought about him she might well be out of a job tomorrow.

'Laura.' His calm voice cut across her thoughts and she was forced to look up at him.

He smiled. 'You have very eloquent eyes, do you know that?' he murmured, a hint of teasing warmth in his gaze. 'Sometimes they seem to speak volumes.'

'Do they?' Her voice was flat. 'And what are they saying now?'

His lips twisted. 'They are calling me a rat. They are telling me that I have a wife and that you don't want anything more to do with me because I'm a cheat.'

'Sounds like you've got a guilty conscience,' Laura said, leaning back in her chair and trying to appear relaxed. Inside she was simmering.

Rogan shook his head and smiled at her. 'That's one thing I don't have.'

'Well, maybe you should.' Laura couldn't resist the gibe and her voice was laced with fury.

'Ah!' A flicker of amusement lit his dark eyes and it made Laura's blood pressure rise dramatically. 'Perhaps I should explain. It was my *ex*-wife who was on the phone earlier. I'm divorced.'

'Your ex-wife?' Laura stared at him and felt the colour return to her skin in one almighty rush. She shook her head. The relief was immense. 'I thought—'

'I know what you thought,' Rogan interrupted smoothly. 'I could see all too clearly what was going through your mind.'

'Well, it's not really any of my business.' Laura tried to sound indifferent.

'No?' Rogan looked at her with a wry lift of one eyebrow. 'So you wouldn't care if I was married?'

'Of course I'd care,' she blurted out furiously. 'I'd never...get involved with a married man.'

He smiled as he saw the colour rise even further beneath her cheeks. 'Last night was fabulous, by the way,' he said in a very low, very husky tone. 'You were probably right to call a halt to things when you did... maybe things are happening a little too quickly between us.'

'Maybe we should just call a halt to the whole thing—'

'I don't want to,' he cut across her quickly, then

frowned. 'I want to continue seeing you, Laura,' he admitted huskily.

Laura's heart thudded unsteadily in her chest. She had been going to say that last night had been a mistake and that it wouldn't happen again, but she couldn't think straight.

He glanced at his watch. 'Look, I can't keep Paul waiting any longer.'

The swift transition from personal conversation to business made her frown.

'Are we still on for Sunday?' he asked her, one hand on the doorhandle.

'Is your wife called Sophie?' she asked, with total disregard for his question or the fact that Paul was waiting for him. She felt she needed to know more before she committed herself to going out with him again. She wasn't sure at all about what had happened between them last night. The fact that he hadn't mentioned that he had been married stung. She felt as if she were now stepping out into totally uncharted territory.

He shook his head. 'Her name is Melony and she's my ex-wife. Sophie is my ex-girlfriend.'

'You seem to have been through a lot of women,' Laura said wryly.

'I did make it clear that I don't go in for serious relationships.' His tone was serious.

She shrugged, but inside her emotions were bobbing up and down. 'Of course you did. And I told you I don't want complications in my life. Which makes me think that both of us nearly took leave of our senses last night.'

'A very pleasurable leave.' He smiled slightly.

'It shouldn't have happened.' She forced herself to say the words. 'I'm glad I called a halt to things because, believe it or not, I don't go in for casual sex.'

The buzzer on her desk broke the tense silence that fell between them. 'That will probably be Karen, looking for me,' Rogan remarked. 'Look, we can't really discuss this here, but I do want you to know that I respect your feelings, Laura.'

Laura stared at him and felt her heart pumping painfully. It was hard to keep a distance between them when he was behaving like the perfect gentleman. 'Can we find some space to discuss this further on Sunday?' he continued gently.

She continued to stare at him.

'You do still want to go out with me on Sunday?' he asked with a frown when she didn't answer him immediately.

For some reason the note of uncertainty in his voice made her throw away caution. 'Yes,' she admitted huskily. 'I do.'

He smiled back. 'I'll pick you and the children up at midday.'

The buzzer rang again. 'I'm sorry, Laura, but I have to go.' He shook his head regretfully. 'Tell Karen I'm on my way, will you?'

He made to open the door, then suddenly stopped and looked back at her. 'By the way, have you mentioned to anyone that we are seeing each other socially?'

'No.'

'Good,' he said. 'Maybe we had better leave it that way. Our private lives are our own business.'

'Fine.' She shrugged and then watched as he walked away from her towards the lifts. She didn't blame him for wanting to keep his private life separate from work and, anyway, she didn't want to be labelled as the boss's mistress. The very thought made her freeze. If she continued on this track it was only a matter of time before he did make her his mistress.

It was all very well for Rogan to tell her that he respected her feelings about casual love-making, but he had also made it clear once again that he didn't want anything deeper than an affair. So where on earth could they go from here?

Laura returned her attention to the drawings on her desk. She should have told him that she didn't want to go out with him on Sunday. That was the only logical thing to do. But she didn't want to be logical.

Deep down warning bells were ringing.

A roaring fire warmed the dining room of the local inn. The place had character, with a low-beamed ceiling and small windows that overlooked the blue Irish Sea.

Sunday lunch had been very pleasant and they had lingered over it. The children were in their element, both vying for Rogan's attention. Matthew told Rogan about his trip to the dentist, and was full of bravado now it was over. Joanne talked about a school trip she wanted to go on.

Laura glanced across and met Rogan's eyes. He had been watching her for the last few minutes, she realised suddenly, as if he was deep in thought.

'Shall we go?' He smiled, making her wonder if she had imagined the intense gaze.

She nodded and he got up from the table to go and pay their bill, with Matthew following.

Laura watched them. Her son looked so small next to Rogan's tall frame. She noticed that he was copying Rogan, standing just as he was, with legs slightly apart and one hand on the top of his back pocket as if he were getting his wallet out.

'Rogan's really nice, isn't he, Mum?' Joanne asked her suddenly. 'I think he's the best boyfriend you've ever gone out with.'

'He's just a friend, Jo,' Laura said firmly, but even as she spoke she was wondering how much longer she could hold on to the pretence of that. Every little glance, ever warm word, made an impact on her.

'Do you think Rogan likes living in that big house of his all alone?' Jo continued, regardless of her mother's statement. 'I mean, he must get lonely, don't you think?'

Laura flicked an amused glance at her daughter. 'No, I think that's the way Rogan wants it. Some people like their space.' She stood to go and get their coats.

It was cold outside, one of those brilliantly blue clear days where the ground was frosty and the air sharp. Laura was glad of her warm cords and suede jacket.

'Are we going to see your horse now?' Matthew asked Rogan as they walked through the little rose garden outside the inn.

'Yes, I thought, if we were all in agreement, we could walk.' He nodded towards a path that led from the car park around the headland. 'The stables are on the other side. It's about two miles.'

'Great.' Matthew was the first to run to the path, his red coat flapping open.

'Zip your coat up,' Laura called after him.

He paid no attention. Maybe he couldn't hear. 'One word from me and he does as he likes,' she said jokingly to Rogan.

'I'll tell him.' Joanne hurried after her brother.

'You don't mind walking?' Rogan asked Laura as they were left alone.

'Not at all.' She glanced up at him. 'Thanks for lunch, it was lovely.'

He didn't answer her and he seemed to be deep in thought again. For a while they walked in silence, watching the children up ahead.

'What are you thinking about?' she asked him suddenly.

'Nothing.' He frowned. That was a lie. He had been thinking about the fact that he had told himself he mustn't see her again yet he seemed incapable of sticking to the resolution.

Yesterday an attractive woman he had taken out once had phoned him and invited him to dinner. Without even the slightest of hesitations, he had politely refused. Even when her voice had been filled with husky inducement he hadn't been in the slightest bit tempted.

All he could think about was Laura…and, worse still, he had found himself worrying about Matthew yesterday, wondering how he had got on at the dentist. He'd had to ring Laura to find out.

He raked an impatient hand through his hair. Laura was getting under his skin. That was definitely against his rules. He'd have to have a wild affair with her and get her out of his system, he decided forcefully.

'Why didn't you tell me you'd been married?' Laura asked him suddenly, breaking into his thoughts.

'It's something I like to forget.' Rogan shrugged.

'Was it that bad?'

'I never want to repeat the experience, put it that way.' His voice was heavy for a second, his eyes distant.

'What happened?'

He flicked a sardonically amused glance down at her. 'She didn't understand me.'

'You mean she didn't understand your affairs?' Laura retorted, irritated by the flippant reply.

'I didn't have affairs,' he said quietly, 'but she left me anyway.'

'I'm sorry.' She took a deep breath. 'I shouldn't have said that.'

He grinned. 'You have a quick Celtic temper, don't you? Your eyes were certainly flashing fire on Friday when you thought I was married.'

'It's little wonder I was annoyed. You should remind your secretary that you no longer have a wife—that she's now your ex-wife.

'Karen is extremely efficient, but that is one mistake she has made many times,' he drawled with lazy amusement.

'It's one way of seeing off unwanted girlfriends, I suppose,' Laura said stiffly. She was still upset by the episode…hurt that Rogan hadn't told her about his past.

'I can do my own, "seeing off", as you call it,' he assured her briskly, 'and I have spoken to Karen about her error.'

'If you'd told me you were divorced it wouldn't have been an issue.'

'It was hardly an issue. It was a small misunderstanding.'

Remembering the shock and the pain she had felt, Laura felt a dart of annoyance. 'Hardly small. Your secrecy left me thinking I'd been consorting with a married man, and that's something I'd never do.' Her voice was low and laced with fury. 'I even started to wonder if you had children tucked away somewhere.'

'I told you I had no children.' He seemed unconcerned.

'You told me you were wary of marriage because your own parents had been through a bitter divorce,' she snapped. 'You forgot to mention you'd been through one yourself.'

He stopped suddenly and turned her to look at him. 'Laura, you're blowing the whole thing out of proportion. I've been married. It's over. It's not a secret, just something I don't like to talk about. Some things are too painful to rake over.'

Laura stared up at him. She could understand that, could even empathise, especially with that momentary raw note in his voice. She looked up at him and her heart melted.

Their breath merged in the frosty air.

'You asked me what I was thinking about earlier,' he murmured in a low tone. 'I was thinking how you are driving me out of my mind,' he admitted softly.

'My Celtic temper is getting to you?' she asked in a mock-playful tone, but deep down she knew exactly what he meant.

'Your curvaceous body, your eyes, your mouth, yes,

even that fiery Celtic temper—everything is getting to me,' he whispered huskily. 'I want you like crazy.'

Her heart pounded. She wanted him, too.

The children's voices, calling them, penetrated hazily through the mist of desire. She pulled away from him. 'We had better keep an eye on them,' she said unsteadily.

Rogan fell into step beside her as she walked on. For a while they walked in silence. The path was close to the sea and the waves were rippling in over the stony shore in a tranquil way, making a soft sucking sound on the pebbles as they withdrew.

'Do you want me, Laura?' he asked gently after a while.

'I'm not sure how I feel.' She took a deep breath and admitted softly, 'The last man I went to bed with was my husband.'

'And you think that giving yourself to me would be disloyal to his memory?'

She smiled at that. 'No...' Nothing could be further from the truth. 'I told you, I just don't go in for casual relationships. I'm a single parent, Rogan. My children are my main priority in life.'

Up ahead Joanne and Matthew were jumping over the rock pools with squeals of laughter.

'I can understand you wanting to protect them—'

'Can you?' She glanced up at him.

He nodded. 'But I think you're hiding behind them now.'

'I'm not.' She was indignant. 'It's very hard, you know, bringing up two children on your own. And they've been through such a lot, with losing their father. I do my best for them but sometimes I wonder if it's enough.' She hesitated for a moment, deep in thought.

'Especially for Matt. There's no doubt that he would have been his father's boy. He loves to talk about sport or cars and planes...' She shook her head. 'I try to keep up an interest in them, but I'm afraid Jo and I are more into the latest fashions.'

Rogan laughed at that and took hold of her hand. 'I think you do a wonderful job,' he said warmly.

The words and the touch of his hand made her heart contract.

'Thanks, but you don't really know me.' She tried to sound sensible.

'I think I do. I think you are scared as hell of giving yourself to me because you don't want to be hurt.' He grinned and admitted huskily, 'And I'm scared as hell of hurting you. That's the main reason I rushed so quickly from your house the other night.'

When she didn't say anything he continued, 'I admit my intentions aren't strictly honourable. I want you as my mistress…not my wife. But I do care about you.'

She smiled at that. 'You're so honest,' she said wryly. Then she looked up at him directly. 'I'll think about it.'

He stared at her. Usually women fell over themselves for him. Laura was so different…so adorable…so maddening.

The children were calling again, and Laura picked up her pace. 'Come on,' she called back to Rogan. 'I'll race you to the end of the path.'

Suddenly they were running after the children and then laughing helplessly with them as they chased them along the shore.

They were all breathless when they finally reached the stables. Laura sat on a fence while Rogan went to organise a ride around the paddock for the children.

Mystic was the most gorgeous thoroughbred, her coat the colour of gold and her mane pure white. Matthew and Joanne fell instantly in love.

'This day is going to be discussed again and again for the next year,' Laura told Rogan when he joined her.

They watched Matthew slide from the horse's back so that the stable girl could help Joanne mount. 'I hope you know you've started something. Matt is now going to add horses to his cars, planes and boats list.'

Rogan laughed. 'I shall take it as a compliment if he does.'

Laura looked across at him. Something about the way he said those words made her heart melt.

'I've got something to ask you,' Rogan said suddenly, his tone serious. 'I probably should wait to discuss this in the office but as we are together...' He shrugged.

She looked at him with a frown.

'I want you to come to New York with me next week.'

Her eyes widened. 'Why?'

'Work, of course.' He grinned, then conceded, 'Although we don't have to rule out having fun.'

'I don't know, Rogan...' Immediately she was wary.

'Before you answer I have to tell you it's a serious business trip. I'm going to include a section on James Home Design in one of the New York stores—soft furnishings with a Celtic theme. I think it will go down well in the American market.'

'And where do I fit in?' Laura was slightly bemused to be talking about big business in such a relaxed way.

'It will be an opportunity for you to meet my other staff, and I'd very much like your input into the designs for the showcase.'

She looked over at him. 'Where would I stay?'

He hesitated. 'Depends on you,' he said huskily. 'You can stay at my apartment or, if you prefer, I'll organise a hotel for you.'

Still she didn't say anything. 'It will be three days, Laura. I think it would be good for you to see how we operate Stateside. It would give a boost to your career.'

'Oh, yes?' She turned to him with eyes that were half smiling, half cautious. 'Are you trying to induce me with bribery, Mr Powers?'

'I think I'd rather induce you with promises of untold pleasures.' He grinned. 'But I assure you this is work.'

'I'll have to check that my mother is free to take care of the children,' she said slowly.

'Fine.' He nodded.

'Then there is the party we are throwing for Robert next Friday. I really should be there.'

'We'll be back for that. It's three days, Tuesday and Wednesday, arriving back Thursday. Laura, I do want you to do this. It's a serious project and I think it could be the link that will strengthen business between Dublin and New York.'

CHAPTER EIGHT

As THE Power company jet banked, ready for descent at JFK airport, Laura felt suddenly very apprehensive.

They had worked throughout the long flight and the paperwork had taken her mind off the more personal side of this trip. But now as she looked across at Rogan she wondered what on earth she was doing here with him.

Rogan packed away the mountain of paperwork he had been working on since take-off from Dublin.

'A bit late, but it was a good flight,' he said nonchalantly as he met Laura's eye.

She nodded, struck afresh by how relaxed he sounded. He had been like this throughout the long flight. Friendly, yet not overly familiar, as if this was all really business and he had no designs on her body.

She should be pleased that they had only discussed work and that the flight had been nothing but paperwork, interspersed with a few meals and polite conversation.

As the noise of the engines increased and the plane descended towards the runway Laura turned to look out of the window. Her first trip to New York. She wished the children were with her.

The thought made her remember their smiling faces when she had told them she was accompanying Rogan on a business trip. They had been so excited for her. Come to that, so had her mother. Cora had instantly volunteered to look after the children.

'You seem to be getting on very well with your new boss,' she had remarked cheerfully.

'I enjoy his company.'

'That means a lot. And the children seem very fond

of him, don't they? Do you think Rogan intends to live full time in Ireland?'

'I don't think so, Mum.'

The conversation had been casual but Laura had known that hidden behind her mother's words was a voice urging caution. A relationship with Rogan could lead nowhere, she knew that, so it was best not to get too involved.

The wheels of the plane touched down smoothly on the runway, jolting Laura from her thoughts. The seat-belt sign went off and Rogan rose to get their belongings together.

'It looks cold out there,' she said, looking out.

'Yes, the snow seems to have come early this year, and the weather forecast is for more of the same.'

Rogan helped her on with her coat, the touch of his hand against her arm sending a wave of desire racing through her.

She watched as he put on the long, dark, Armani coat over his dark business suit.

Hell, he was gorgeous, she thought suddenly. The smart suit, the dark hair with just a few strands of grey at the temple, the dark eyes and square jaw just seemed to scream sensuality.

He looked over at her and smiled and her heart seemed to go into overdrive.

It astonished her that she should have to fight so hard for control every time Rogan so much as glanced at her or touched her. It frightened her.

'Did you book a hotel room for me?' she asked him suddenly. She tried to sound casual but her apprehension showed in her voice.

He smiled. 'I will if you want me to, Laura. Or there's a spare room at my apartment. We'll talk about the sleeping arrangements later, shall we?'

He was so cool.

'If you want.' She tried to match his urbane indifference, but her voice wasn't entirely convincing.

There was a gleam in his eye, as if he found her endearing.

He knew, she thought suddenly. He knew that she was weakening towards him...that there was a part of her that wanted to throw caution away.

All she needed to do was say that she wanted him, and he would take her back to his apartment and make love to her... She had no doubts about that.

Of course, it would mean nothing...but it would, in all certainty, feel wonderful. Just to be held close in his arms, to be stroked tenderly and kissed...

She turned from him.

The doors of the plane were opened and they stepped into the wintry New York morning.

She felt both excitement and apprehension as they cleared immigration. She wondered suddenly if Rogan had got her here under false pretences, if there was no work involved at all?

The thought was very disquieting. Then she remembered they had been doing costings all the way from Dublin airport. Of course this was business. She felt foolish for a moment. Rogan was charming and seductive, but he was a straightforward businessman. And he had never lied to her.

He had made it clear that he wanted to sleep with her, but it was up to her. And he hadn't tried to pretend to her that he was looking for serious involvement.

A limousine met them at the airport and they sat in silence for a while as it whisked them towards Manhattan.

'Are you all right, Laura?' Rogan asked, as he opened his briefcase to read through some files.

'Yes, of course.'

His eyes moved over her gently, as if noticing the strain in her eyes and the tense way she was sitting so far from him on the long seat. 'I'll be finished with this paperwork soon. The more I can get done while we're travelling the more free time I can grab later.'

Free time for what? The question blazed through her. 'That's fine,' she answered, trying to sound indifferent.

She turned her head and looked out at the New York skyline. It was spectacular. Buildings towered into the ice-blue sky and glass shimmered in the early morning sunlight. A light covering of snow was on the pavements. People were well wrapped up against the weather in fur coats and woollen hats. She noticed the food stalls and the wafts of steam that seemed to rise mysteriously from the road.

They drove along Fifth Avenue and she leaned forward, craning her neck to look at the shop windows.

They passed Tiffany's, Trump Tower. She was truly in New York and it was just as she had imagined it— better, in fact.

The limousine slowed as they reached Central Park.

'Almost home,' Rogan said with a smile as he started to put his work back in his briefcase.

'Home?' She looked at him with a frown.

'Yes, I thought we would call at my apartment first and freshen up, before going in to the office. You can check in at your hotel later if you want.'

Home for Rogan Powers was an enormous penthouse on the top floor of a twenty-storey building.

Wooden floors and white walls added to the feeling of space. It was all very ultra-modern and uncluttered. Modern expressionist and abstract paintings hung on the walls, and occasional furniture was in glass and chrome. The only colour to be seen, apart from the paintings, was the green of large plants and the beige and tan of leather upholstery.

Laura couldn't help comparing it with her home. Suddenly she had the feeling that she wouldn't fit very easily into Rogan's high-flying, sophisticated world. She liked chintz and warm floral tones. Rogan was the extreme opposite.

'You don't need me to design the decor for this place,' she said in admiration. 'It's lovely.'

'In keeping with the surroundings, I suppose,' he said.

'Who looks after it for you?' she asked as he opened the door to a kitchen that was whiter than white with tubular steel stools and chrome pans.

'I have a housekeeper who comes in daily.' Rogan went across to put some coffee on. 'Are you hungry?'

'No, thanks. I ate enough on the plane.' Laura's attention was taken by a bowl of red tulips on the kitchen counter. There was a note propped up against it. She could read it, without picking it up. It said, 'Welcome Home, Love Sarah.'

Immediately Laura felt a thrust of jealousy. Whoever had written the note must be pretty close to Rogan—and must have a key to his apartment.

'Your housekeeper has left you a love note,' she said lightly.

He looked at the flowers and came across to pick up the note. He smiled. 'It's not from my housekeeper,' he said quietly.

Laura fought with herself not to ask, and when he didn't immediately volunteer the information she felt slightly annoyed.

'Did…did you say there was somewhere I could freshen up?' she asked him, wanting to get away from his disturbing presence for a while.

He smiled. 'Sure.' He led the way back out into the corridor and picked up her suitcase to carry it towards a room at the far end.

'And the flowers, by the way, are from my sister. She only lives a few blocks away.'

'You didn't need to explain.' Now that he had she was perversely pretending to be indifferent. But the truth was that she felt tremendously relieved. She really hadn't liked the idea of any other woman having the run of Rogan's apartment. It smacked too much of permanency. She didn't analyse her feelings...she didn't dare.

'Maybe I can meet your sister while we are here,' she ventured cautiously.

'I don't know if we will have time.'

'So it's going to be all work, then?'

'With a little time left over for getting to know each other better,' he said as he opened the door into a large bedroom.

Picture windows looked out over Manhattan. The bed was enormous with an ornate wrought-iron frame.

Was this where he wanted to get to know her? The thought tumbled into her mind from nowhere.

'You've got fabulous views,' Laura said, for want of something better to say.

'They are even better at night.'

'I'll take your word for it,' Laura said, 'but I'll probably be at a hotel...won't I?'

Their eyes met and he grinned as if she thoroughly amused him. He put her suitcase down and opened the door to an *en suite* bathroom. 'There will be plenty of hot water so feel free to take a shower. That way we can go straight on to the office.'

The shrill tone of the phone interrupted them. 'Make yourself at home,' he said as he left her.

She opened her luggage and found a trouser suit in soft cream, which she put on a hanger in the bathroom so that the steam of her shower would help eliminate any creases.

Once she was dressed she inspected her appearance in the mirror, before going back out to Rogan.

She looked stylish. Her hair was sitting perfectly and her make-up was light, yet gave her a healthy glow.

No one looking at her would have guessed that she was a woman who had just made a transatlantic flight.

She walked back through the apartment and found

Rogan at the dining-room table, looking out over the skyscrapers and the distant green of Central Park.

He got to his feet as she joined him. 'I've made coffee. Would you like some?'

'Thank you.' She sat and looked out at the view. 'Wow, this city is even more fantastic than I had imagined.'

'If we've got any spare time I'll show you around.'

Laura looked back at him and their eyes held for a moment. She'd like that, she realised, but she would have preferred to have met his sister. Obviously he hadn't been keen on that idea. Maybe it smacked too much of intimacy for him.

It didn't matter, she told herself firmly. She was here on business.

Rogan's offices were in the financial quarter of the city. They were much bigger and more impressive than the offices in Dublin, Laura thought as they walked into the marble foyer and then went straight up to the fortieth floor.

She took off her coat and hat as the heat started to thaw her out. She was very glad she was wearing a smart suit. Rogan's staff were all very stylishly dressed.

Rogan got someone to show Laura around while he went into a private meeting with two of his chief accountants. When she came back to his office they all rose politely.

'Gentlemen, I'd like to introduce Laura Taylor,' Rogan said smoothly. 'She's going to be lending her expertise to the Celtic range for our store on Fifth Avenue.'

They shook hands with her then settled back into the leather chairs as the girl who had shown Laura around poured them all coffee.

Laura took in the stylish decor and a view of Manhattan which was truly magnificent.

However, there was little time to admire the view. Rogan launched straight into an in-depth discussion on the project, a discussion that lasted two hours and was so intense that Laura's head was swimming with details when it had finished.

After that she was whisked away to the department store to look around the space available for their display. Rogan didn't come with her. He said he'd see her at the offices at the Fifth Avenue store a little later.

It was seven-thirty when she had finished. The light had faded outside, leaving the lights of the skyscrapers twinkling against the dark velvet of the sky.

She didn't realise how late it was until Rogan put his head around the door of the office she was using. 'How's it going?' he asked gently.

Laura smiled. She was really excited about this assignment. It had been great, working with so many different talented designers. 'Your timing is impeccable. I've just finished.'

'Really?' He crossed the room and stood behind her to read the figures she had scribbled down and the preliminary sketches.

'You've done well,' he said, and she could hear by his tone of voice that he was impressed. She smiled, feeling pleased with herself.

'At least I'm on target now. I should finish here tomorrow.'

'Good.' He reached across and switched off the desk light. 'So how about joining me for dinner?'

She turned in her chair and looked up at him. The semi-darkness of the room lent an intimate atmosphere.

'I don't know, Rogan. I have to check into my hotel.'

'We'll have dinner first, then back to my apartment to pick up your luggage.'

'You sound as if you've got it all worked out.'

'I have.' He reached out and took hold of her hand.

'And I've got a wonderful restaurant in mind for you. The perfect place to unwind.'

The touch of his hand against hers set off all kinds of tremors inside her, but she allowed him to pull her to her feet.

'It sounds good.' They were standing very close, perhaps too close, but she felt incapable of moving away.

He smiled and reached for her coat.

They took a yellow cab outside the offices and it slipped into the grid of traffic.

Despite her busy day and all the travel, Laura didn't feel tired but exuberant and alive. New York seemed to be vibrating with excitement and she was happy to be a part of it.

When they reached their destination and got out into the cool night air Laura shivered. Immediately Rogan put an arm around her.

She liked the feeling. She liked being close to him, and found herself remembering the way they had woken up together at Fitzroy's, the immediate feeling of sensuality…and belonging. The way he had kissed her.

The idea of waking up with him again, but this time making love, was so urgent that there was a part of her that wanted to say, Hey, let's forget dinner.

She looked up at him and he smiled. And Laura knew she was falling in love with Rogan Powers. The truth was so startling that she almost caught her breath.

When had that happened? She shook her head, feeling dazed. Had it been when they had been alone together at the castle? Or when she had watched him talking to her children and had felt as if some circle had been completed—as if the four of them were like a family.

Yes…possibly then. She shivered and he drew her even closer against his body. 'Cold?'

She nodded and allowed him to hold her. But she wasn't cold, she was afraid. Afraid of where this was leading.

She couldn't fall in love with Rogan. He would be horrified. If he even suspected that she felt like this he would end things with her here and now.

No, she'd have to forget her feelings, bury them back where they had come from, because they would lead to nothing but heartache.

CHAPTER NINE

THE restaurant was excellent. Not only was the food good but the setting was breathtaking. Yet afterwards, when Laura thought about it, all she could remember was Rogan. She wouldn't have been able to tell anyone what she had eaten.

They sat at a window seat, and the views down towards the street, where the traffic flowed in long straight lines of yellow and red lights, made her feel dizzy.

A dance floor was lit by the glitter of subdued lighting and a small band was playing for the few couples dancing.

Most of the way through the meal Laura managed to keep the conversation on the work she had done that day.

Then Rogan sighed and leaned back in his chair. 'I think we have talked enough about that project for one day. If I'm honest, I never wanted to talk about it tonight in the first place.'

Her heart thudded rapidly as she looked across at him. 'What do you want to talk about?'

'You.'

'That's not such an exciting subject,' she said with a small smile.

'It is to me.'

For a moment his eyes moved over the porcelain paleness of her skin and the wide beauty of her eyes.

'Why don't we talk about you instead?' she asked lightly. 'You never did tell me about your ex-wife.'

'Now there's a subject to dampen the proceedings.'

She toyed with the wine glass in front of her. 'Was the marriage that bad?'

'It started out all right. I don't know, I guess I just got married too young. I was twenty-three. A very ambitious twenty-three. If the truth be told, I had an eye on achievements and not on my marriage.'

'So what happened?' she asked gently.

'The old story. I was out, making money, and she was home, making out. With a guy who called himself my friend.' Rogan shrugged. 'But I suppose it takes two to make a lousy marriage, and I did neglect her. I had a computer programming company at the time and it consumed a lot of my time and energy. I thought she was as dedicated to making a success of things as I was. But I was wrong. She was interested in the money and the lifestyle, but nothing else.'

She heard the pain in his voice and her heart ached with sympathy for him. 'Do you still love her?'

He shook his head. 'No…I got over that a long time ago. At least we didn't have children. It's one thing to mess up your own life but I wouldn't want to have pulled children through the trauma. But I've learnt from my mistakes—I'd never go through that again.'

'Never get married again?'

As soon as she spoke the words she regretted them. He looked across at her and grinned. 'I guess I've got used to being on my own. I was married five years, and I've been divorced eight.'

'Somehow I thought it was more recent than that.' Laura frowned. 'How come your ex-wife still phones you?'

'I gave her shares in the company as part of our divorce settlement. I'm now in a position to buy them back.' Rogan spread his hands. 'I'm in the middle of heavy negotiations with her at the moment.'

Laura noticed the serious look in his eyes now, the note of determination in his voice. 'You are still the

ambitious person with an eye to achievements?' she said
with a smile.

'I suppose I must be. The company is all-important to
me—' He broke off. 'We're talking about business
again!'

'Sorry.' She smiled at him. 'It's my fault. I was curious.'

'Talking about being curious, what was Paul James
talking to you about in the office the other day? I've
noticed that every time he comes into the office he heads
straight for you.'

'We were just discussing Robert's retirement party.'
Laura suddenly remembered the invitation Paul had is-
sued to her to accompany him to that party. She frowned
at the memory.

She wouldn't mention the planned date, she decided
swiftly. In fact, maybe she would ring Paul and have a
quiet word to see if he would mind if she didn't accompany him on the night of the party. She was sure he
wouldn't—they didn't have that kind of relationship.

'Paul went with you to the Fitzroy castle the first time,
didn't he?' Rogan recalled.

She nodded. 'We were kept late…but not as late as
you and I.' She met his eyes across the table.

'He didn't get to wake up with you,' Rogan said
huskily. 'Poor Paul. Now I feel sorry for him. You look
very beautiful first thing in the morning, Laura Taylor.'

She tried not to feel embarrassed by the compliment.
'I'm sure I looked no such thing, but you really do know
all the right things to say,' she murmured.

'Perhaps the time for talking is past…'

For a second her heart missed a beat as she wondered
what he was leading up to, then he grinned teasingly.
'So how about having a dance with me instead?'

Laura hesitated. The band was playing a Nat King
Cole number, 'Unforgettable.'

He stood and held out his hand.

Slowly she got up and allowed him to lead her out to the dance floor.

A tremor raced through her body as he took her into his arms. One hand rested against the soft material of her blouse, and she could feel it burning through to the soft skin beneath.

As a saxophone played they swayed together. Laura rested her head against his jacket. She imagined she could hear the steady thud of his heart.

His hand stroked her gently, a whisper-soft caress that heightened her awareness of him, bringing it to an unbearable ache of sweet yearning.

He bent his head towards hers. 'Sweet Laura.' His voice was a mere husky murmur against her ear. 'I'd like to have a million nights like this one.'

She closed her eyes, breathing in his closeness and his words and storing them away to be treasured, to be remembered, for ever.

As the music finished Rogan released her from the warm circle of his arms and she felt bereft suddenly. She had never wanted anyone the way she wanted Rogan.

'How are you feeling?' Rogan asked as they went back to their table. 'Are you tired?'

'Not too bad, considering I should have jet lag,' she said with a smile.

'Maybe we should go.' Rogan's voice was thick with desire.

Laura knew that hidden beneath the words was the invitation to his bed. Should they go back to his apartment and make love? She felt her heart miss a beat... and knew that was what she wanted.

She met his eyes, so incredibly wonderful. Gentle, passionate. She couldn't find her voice. Anyway, she was scared that if she spoke he would hear the desire that was eating through her so she simply nodded.

They didn't speak at all on the cab ride back to Rogan's apartment. Rogan's arm rested lightly around

her shoulders but to Laura it was like a band of posses-
sion.

She needed to think sensibly about this, she tried to
tell herself sternly. She needed to be sure that she was
doing the right thing.

But how could anyone be sure? She had dated John
for six months and had thought she knew him.

What would she have to lose by sleeping with Rogan?
a small treacherous voice inside asked.

She was a grown woman. Surely she could handle her
emotions, keep them in check. She could handle an affair—take whatever Rogan had to offer her.

By the time they reached the front door of Rogan's
apartment her emotions were torn apart with doubt...
with need.

Rogan flicked a switch and a few lamps lit the room
with an intimate glow. 'Would you like a drink?'

'I don't know... Perhaps I should just collect my case
and go...'

'Is that what you want?'

She met his dark eyes. 'No...' Her heart was thudding
so unevenly against her chest that it was painful.

He pulled her to him and found her lips. His mouth
was gentle, persuasive, against hers. 'I want you so
much, Laura, but I don't want to hurry things between
us, not if you're not ready. I know you like to do things
correctly...' He trailed off, a teasing note in his voice.

She smiled, a gentle, reflective smile. 'I just thought
we should get to know each other better before we took
things any further,' she whispered.

He smiled. 'I've got a bottle of champagne in the
fridge. Shall we start getting to know each other a little
better over a glass of Moët?'

'What about my hotel room?' She hoped she didn't
sound as breathless as she felt.

'We can get to know each other back there if you

want.' He grinned teasingly as he saw the heat racing into her cheeks.

'That's not what I meant—'

'I know.' He placed a soothing finger against her lips for a moment. 'I know what you meant, but I don't want you to go to a hotel. If you really feel you must, you can have the spare bedroom, Laura. I'm not going to force you into anything you don't want.'

She liked the fact that he wasn't going to hurry anything. She felt as if he was allowing her to dictate the pace of the way things went, and it eased her doubts.

'What I want to do…and what I ought to do seem to be two entirely different things,' she said in a low tone. 'Let's have that champagne and talk about it.'

She took off her coat and moved towards the windows to admire the night view of Manhattan. Then turned as she heard Rogan coming back into the room with the champagne, and as she did she noticed there was a red light on his telephone. Immediately she thought about the children.

'Someone has left a message on your answerphone.'

'Yes, I noticed.' He uncorked the bottle of champagne and poured it into two crystal flutes.

'Aren't you going to see who it is? It could be important. It could be my mother.'

'If it's important they'll phone back,' he said, handing her drink across. 'And it won't be your mother.'

'How do you know?' She frowned.

'Because I didn't give you my home number for her. I gave you my work number.' He held up a hand as she made a noise of protest. 'That's not as terrible as it sounds,' he assured her quickly. 'I have a member of staff on my switchboard twenty-four hours a day. And I have a pager with me at all times. That means no matter where we are—out having dinner, even in a taxi—the children can reach us. It made sense to give her that number rather than this one.'

'Oh.' She sat on one of the leather settees. Thinking about the children had brought some sense of responsibility back to her mind.

He sat next to her. 'Now you are thinking about Joanne and Matthew, aren't you? Worrying about them.'

'No, I know they are in safe hands and I rang earlier.' She smiled, then there was a moment's silence before she admitted, 'Well, maybe I am a little worried. You know, it's hard to switch off from the responsibility of children. When they aren't with you it's like some string is pulling you back, making you constantly think about them.' She was quiet for a moment, thinking about her life.

'It's right that your children should be at the top of your list of priorities but you have needs, too, Laura. You shouldn't overlook them.'

She met his eyes and her lips curved in a tremulous smile.

'Is that a purely unselfish remark?'

'No,' he said, 'but at least I'm honest. I told you I'd never knowingly hurt you Laura. On the other hand, I would never make promises I couldn't keep.'

'You mean, if you were to take me to bed it's not because you love me but because you desire me.' Her voice was flat. 'I think I've figured that out by now, Rogan.'

'If it means anything, I am crazy about you…'

She shook her head. 'I wouldn't fool myself that that means anything at all.'

He tipped her chin so that he could look into her eyes. The strange half-light seemed to illuminate the glitter in his eyes and his strong bone structure.

She shivered as his finger moved down to her neck.

'I'm not so sure. I've never wanted any woman the way I want you.'

Her breathing felt restricted. He was so close and she felt so much for him. He leaned closer and kissed her.

She returned his kiss, her heart now slamming furiously. Did he mean it...?

He took her champagne from her hand and placed it on the table.

'Now, where was I?' Rogan murmured huskily as he reached once more to take her in his arms. Laura closed her eyes as his head lowered towards hers again. Her whole body felt alive with longing.

When their lips met again the feeling was electric. This time the gentleness was replaced with a fierce, bitter-sweet longing. Laura felt his hands move around her and draw her closer. His hand stroked her back then moved upwards to sweep the heaviness of her hair back from her face as he kissed her neck.

'I want you so much, Laura,' he murmured against her ear.

She felt her defences crumbling...felt the heat of desire start to take over. Her whole body was alive with a vibrant, passionate need.

'I want you, too,' she murmured, the words almost incoherent.

Only when Rogan pulled away from her slightly to look down into her eyes did she become aware that she had spoken aloud the words that were drumming throughout her entire body.

'Do you mean it?'

Trembling, she nodded her head, not trusting herself to speak. He put a hand under her chin and tipped her head up so that he could look into her eyes, then he smiled as if what he saw pleased him more than the words she had spoken. Softly, he kissed her lips.

As he did so she felt him unbuttoning her blouse. She wasn't wearing a bra and, feeling suddenly shy, she put up a hand to stop the silky material from falling.

He kissed her neck, then her ear, his hands stroking her naked back. Then gently he uncurled her fingers, allowing the material to slither downwards.

She shivered, and snuggled closer against the warmth of his body. She wasn't cold—the fire that was blazing through her was much much too strong. Her shivers were a mixture of desire and apprehension. It had been so long since she'd trusted a man, so long since she had wanted unreservedly to give herself like this.

His hands stroked the narrow curve of her waist and he made no attempt to move her away from him. He just held her.

'You're not nervous, are you?' he whispered against her neck, sending delicious little shivers of desire shuddering through her.

'A little,' she acknowledged softly. 'It's been a long time.'

'I won't hurt you...I promise.'

Laura knew that Rogan would be a skilled and sensitive lover—she had no doubts about that. It was her emotions that she worried about. She cuddled closer, hearing the steady beat of his heart against her ear.

It was delicious to be held like this. She felt cherished...loved. The words rang inside her and even as she acknowledged how foolish they were the feeling refused to die. She had never felt like this before. She felt protected inside the warm circle of his arms.

Then he picked her up and carried her through to the bedroom. He didn't turn on a light. The city lights lit the room in a kaleidoscope of colour against the stark white of the sheets on his bed.

He placed her on the bed, then his hands moved to take the rest of her clothing off.

'Let me look at you,' he said, his voice a husky rasp as he caressed her naked skin.

Her long, dark hair lay in a swathe across the perfect smoothness of her skin. Her figure was curvaceous, with high, full breasts above a taut ribcage, small waist and gently curved hips.

'You're so beautiful.' He breathed the words in a seductive whisper. Reaching out, he stroked her breast. The nipples were hard and erect with desire and she shuddered with pleasure. Slowly, he bent his head to touch his lips to her breast.

'Laura, I'm too impatient for you.' She felt his hands against the silk of her underwear, pulling them down. 'I want you now.'

The feeling was mutual. Laura felt that if he didn't make love to her straight away she would go crazy with desire. She watched as he took off his tie, then started to unbutton his shirt. She reached out to curl her fingers through the dark hair on his chest, then slid her hand lower to rest on his flat, tightly muscled stomach.

She felt his muscles contract at her gentle touch and she smiled, filled suddenly with a tremendous sense of power that she could turn him on so easily. She bent and pressed her lips where her hands had been, breathing in the clean, musky scent of him.

Rogan gave a low growl of desire deep in his throat and bent to kiss her lips with fervent passion, his hands caressing her breasts—teasing her nipples until they were so hard she felt she would burst.

He took off the rest of his clothing and then his legs straddled her hips as he knelt over her. She arched her back in longing, aching for the full force of him to touch her.

'Patience,' he growled teasingly, then kissed each of her breasts, sucking at them and licking at them until she cried out for him in desperate anguish.

'Not yet,' he murmured silkily as he kissed her stomach. Then his fingers moved to stroke the soft, wet core of her womanhood.

Every part of her throbbed with the most piercing desire. She wanted him, she needed him. If he didn't enter her soon she was going to explode without him. She raked her hand through her hair, pulling it back from her scalp in a kind of frenzied frustration. The action lifted her breasts even higher and he lent to lick at them with the tip of his tongue.

'Rogan, I can't wait any longer, I just can't.' Her voice trembled with urgency.

As she spoke he reached toward the bedside table for something. Seconds later he was inside her. Great shudders of pleasure ripped through her entire body.

He sat above her and watched the way she writhed under him. He pushed deeper and deeper, stroking her body in a way that sent her almost wild.

Just when she thought she couldn't take any more he controlled the moment, leaving her frantic with longing. Then he built the momentum again as she cried out his name in gasps of yearning. This time there was no holding back. He thrust into her, allowing their passion full rein, as they rocked together in spasm after spasm of complete fulfilment.

CHAPTER TEN

THE noise of traffic twenty floors below them filtered through the double-glazed windows. Laura lay, listening to the distant hum. She saw the sun strengthening from weak red-gold to blazing yellow across the white walls and carpets.

She stretched luxuriously in the enormous bed and turned to look at Rogan. He was lying on his side, facing her, still in a deep sleep.

It was no wonder he was tired, she thought, a smile curving the softness of her lips. They had been very...very energetic last night. And it had been wonderful, she thought dreamily...perfect.

The sheets were low on his waist. He looked very tanned against their whiteness, the hair on his chest extremely dark.

Impulsively she reached out to stroke that coarse hair, remembering how it had felt against the softness of her breasts last night.

He opened his eyes and looked directly into hers. 'Laura?' His voice was a gruff, seductive sound.

Her heart lurched crazily, tipping and tilting as if she were on some kind of fairground ride.

'Last night was fabulous.'

'Yes,' she agreed, and leaned closer to kiss his lips. They were warm against hers, and inviting.

'Mmm.' He made a guttural sound deep in his throat which seemed to inflame her all over again.

Her breath caught, and she rolled closer. She could feel her whole body pressing against his, could feel the muscular strength of him. He smiled and caught her in powerful arms to roll her on top of him.

She could feel his arousal and she smiled, feeling shy...pleased...overwhelmed by him. 'Do you think it's possible to have too much of a good thing?'

He reached up and raked his fingers through the thick glossy fall of her hair. 'I can never have too much of you...never.'

The sound of the telephone was an unwelcome intrusion. Its shrill ring filled the silence between their raging heartbeats and their desire.

'Damn it all!'

'Don't answer it,' Laura said, and bent to kiss his cheek, then his chin, working her way around to his lips.

'I'll have to.' He reached to snatch up the receiver.

Much as she was disappointed that he had picked up the receiver, she had to smile at the note in his voice. She had caused that growl, that tremor in his voice. He had wanted her as much as she wanted him.

'No, it's all right. I'll see you later.' He slammed down the phone.

'Who was it?'

'The damn office. I'll have to go in straight away.' He turned his head to look at the clock, then sighed. 'It's still very early, I'm sorry, Laura, this has messed up our morning.'

'It's OK. Another ten minutes and we'll both go.'

'No point you coming in this early.' His eyes darkened and his hands curved around her breast. 'Besides, I think you had better lie here for a while and regain your strength. You might need it later.'

'I have got a busy day ahead of me.' Laura grinned.

'I wasn't thinking about work,' Rogan assured her. 'I was thinking about ravishing your body again as soon as is decently possible. Even if that means making love to you on my desk.'

'Rogan!' She was half amused, half shocked.

He smiled. 'I love the way you can sound so prim and proper and act like a wildcat in bed,' he murmured teasingly. 'It really turns me on.'

Laura felt her skin heat up at those words and he laughed then kissed her forcefully and possessively on the lips, before rolling her away from him and getting out of bed.

He disappeared into the bathroom and she heard the sound of the shower. She couldn't help feeling disappointed. She had hoped that they would have a few hours together before work encroached.

When he came back into the bedroom he was wearing just a towel around his waist. For a moment she was reminded of that morning at the castle when he had walked into the bedroom like this. In a way she wished their affair had started back then. She wanted to know so much about Rogan, wanted to melt into his life.

'I'll leave the address of the office on the dressing-table,' he said nonchalantly, 'then you can follow me down at your leisure. Get a cab.'

She watched as he dressed in a smart dark grey suit. He came to sit on the edge of the bed to look down at her. 'Will you be all right? You know you have to keep alert in New York—'

'I am not a country bumpkin,' she said forcefully.

'I know you are an intelligent woman. I'm just reminding you to be careful.' He bent and kissed her lips tenderly.

A flare of longing, so piercing and acute, took her breath away.

'Now, you do know where you are?' he asked as he straightened.

'Yes, I'm in your bed...' she reached up and touched the side of his face '...where I wish you were.'

He smiled, a tender indulgent smile, as he took in the beauty of her features—the way her eyes seemed suddenly too large for her face, the softness of her lips, the blush of colour on her high cheek-bones. 'I wish I was staying there with you,' he assured her, bending to kiss her once more. 'But I can't,' he finished regretfully as he stood up.

Laura's mouth tingled from the touch of his lips, and her body cried out for him.

He opened the bedside table and bent to search through some papers. 'Here we are.' He took something out and put it next to the phone. 'A map and the address and phone number of my office. Now, have you got enough money?'

'Rogan!' Her voice rose in sharp annoyance. 'If you are going to go, just go.'

'I'm going.' He held up his hands in mock surrender. 'Just be careful.'

'It's a bit late for that, isn't it?' She couldn't help the words as she remembered last night.

He grinned. 'You've got nothing to worry about. I always practise safe sex.'

Before she could say anything to that he had gone. She supposed she had asked for that comment, she thought angrily. She shouldn't have made such a flippant remark.

She lay, staring up at the ceiling. Why should those few little words upset her so? After all, it had just been a statement of fact—nothing derogatory, nothing to suggest he regretted what had happened between them. Even so, the mere word 'practise' irritated her intensely. He made it sound as if he were playing with her until the real thing came along. Then there was the word 'sex'. Why couldn't he have said 'love-making'?

She rolled on her side and closed her eyes but she couldn't relax. She was wide awake now. She got up and went through to have a shower, then she dressed in a long, dark skirt and a silk fitted top in cream, before going through to the lounge.

The champagne glasses were where they had left them

last night, the bottle of champagne still almost full. She went across to pick them up and as she passed she noticed that the red light was no longer on the answer-machine.

Had Rogan listened to his message? She hadn't heard him.

Something made her pause by the phone. She looked down at it, hesitated and then, before she could think better of her action, she pressed the play button.

A woman's voice filled the room, tearful, accusing, pleading. 'Rogan, it's Sophie. I know you are home. Why don't you return my calls? Please, Rogan... I love you.'

The tape switched off and rewound, the whirring, mechanical noises the machine made as it reset itself resounding in the silence of the apartment.

Laura stood where she was for several long moments. She felt shocked at the anguish she could hear in the woman's voice—shocked and, to some degree, sympathetic. She turned, picked up her bag and her coat and left the apartment.

She went straight to work. She didn't know what else to do with herself and it seemed safer to bury her mind in the designs for the Celtic range rather than go over and over the chilling memory of Sophie's voice.

When Rogan heard that she was in he came across to her office.

'I thought you wouldn't be in until at least ten o'clock.'

'I've got a lot to do before we leave for Dublin tomorrow.' She barely looked up at him. She couldn't bring herself to meet his eyes.

'Is everything all right?' He came closer, the warmth of concern in his voice making her emotions cloud with confusion.

'Yes.' Her voice was sharper than she'd intended. 'Of course. I've just got a lot of work to get through.' She forced herself to regain control and soften her tone. 'And I'd like to gain some time to look around the shops later. I want to buy the children something.'

'OK.' He seemed to think this was perfectly reasonable. 'I'll catch up with you later. I've got to go, Laura. I'm in the middle of a meeting.'

'Yes, fine.'

He hesitated for a moment then he closed the door behind him. Laura let out her breath in a long, shuddering sigh. Then she turned her attention to the papers in front of her and tried to blank everything else out of her mind.

As far as work was concerned, the day went smoothly. Maybe because Laura was so determined not to let her mind wander from her job she finished it with a single-minded attempt at perfection. The designs and the costings were printed out and checked by three-thirty, leaving Laura free to leave the building.

Rogan had been astounded when she had walked in and put it on his desk. 'You've finished!'

'That's right.' Laura had been brisk. 'I'm going to wander along Fifth Avenue now and do some shopping, if that's all right with you.'

'Yes.' He looked up at her, his eyes moving over the slender lines of her body, and she knew that he was wishing they were alone, that the team of accountants in his office could be melted away.

Laura didn't know how she felt. In one way she was glad that he hadn't had a chance to talk to her in that seductive tone of his. In another way, like him, she just wanted everyone to go away.

He glanced at his watch. 'If you'd like, I'll meet you at the Rockefeller Centre for coffee. I should be finished here soon...so, say five o'clock.'

'OK.' She turned and left the office, but was surprised when he followed her out.

'Laura.'

She looked around at him.

'Do you have that map that I gave you this morning?'

'Yes.' She was acutely conscious of his two secretaries, watching them with interest from their desks. She wondered bleakly how many of Rogan's women had passed through this way. His secretaries probably had to screen calls from girlfriends he was no longer interested in.

'See you later.' Not giving him a chance to say anything else, she left the office.

Even after work, the freezing cold air and a walk around some of the busiest shops in the world Laura still hadn't got that phone call out of her mind.

She sat, drinking coffee and watching the people at the Rockefeller Centre, and tried not to think any more about it, but somehow she couldn't get it out of her mind.

She put her hands around her coffee-cup in a vain attempt to warm herself up.

She should forget about Sophie, she told herself crossly. It was none of her business—she should never have listened to that tape. Lord alone knew what had possessed her to turn it on.

What had Rogan said about Sophie? She racked her memory to remember. Nothing much, just that she was an ex-girlfriend. She had presumed that the woman had been way back in his past but now she remembered that he still wore the gift she had given him—the gold Cartier watch.

Maybe the affair had been recent and Rogan had only just dropped her when he'd gone to Ireland.

Sophie was probably someone like her, someone who had given herself to Rogan in the hope that he might feel something for her. Laura swallowed hard. She would never, ever, beg Rogan to get in contact with her, she told herself fiercely. Never. When he moved on to his next conquest she would melt quietly into the background. She had her pride.

'You found your way around all right.' Rogan's hand pressed warmly on her shoulder as he walked up behind her. He bent to kiss her cheek and she forced herself not to pull away.

'Of course I found my way around. Did you ever doubt it?' She tried to sound light-hearted, as if she hadn't a care in the world.

'No...never.' He picked his way around the mound of shopping bags at her feet and pulled out a chair opposite her.

'I see you've bought out New York, single-handed,' he observed with a grin.

'I can flex my plastic with the best.' She tried not to think about how handsome he looked. He was wearing his heavy overcoat over his suit and a lock of his dark hair was resting on his forehead. She longed to reach across and brush it back with tender fingers, but clamped her hands tighter around her cup.

'Did you buy anything for yourself?'

'I got some things for the house.' Laura shrugged. 'There are presents for Joanne and Matthew and my mother...'

'I thought so.'

Should she ask him about Sophie? The answer was immediate and vehement. No, definitely not. He would only think her possessive and jealous. Rogan would be the type to panic at possessiveness. She knew that as surely as she knew how much she loved him.

'That's why I decided to buy you a present.'

She watched as he reached into the inside pocket of his overcoat, took out a long box and handed it across to her.

'"Tiffany's".' She read the lettering in a flat, unemotional voice as she took it from him.

He watched as she opened it.

Inside a diamond necklace glittered as the cold sunlight hit it. It was, without a doubt, the most beautiful piece of jewellery Laura had ever seen, and it must have cost a fortune. She stared at it for a long moment, not knowing what to say.

'Do you like it?' he asked. 'If not, we can go back and change it for something else.'

'It's beautiful.'

'No, you are beautiful.' He stretched out a hand and lifted her chin, forcing her to look up and meet his eyes across the table. 'Exquisite, in fact,' he murmured huskily.

'What is it for?'

He frowned as he heard the brittle note creep into her voice. 'It's for you...'

'As a thank-you or a goodbye?'

He stared at her in perplexity for a moment, taking in the shadows in her eyes and the way she held her head, proud and yet at the same time defenceless. 'It's neither.' He shook his head. 'What's got into you, Laura? It's a present from me to you. No strings, no hidden agenda—just a present.'

She swallowed hard. 'No strings, no hidden agenda,' she repeated, and then closed the box with a snap. 'Of course. I didn't expect strings. I know you don't like them. Do you, Rogan?'

'Do you want to tell me what this is about?' he asked, his voice lower and suddenly very serious, 'because I feel as if I've missed something.'

'You missed a phone call.' All Laura's good intentions were suddenly tossed aside. She never had been one for holding in her feelings, she thought despairingly. If she had something to say she had to say it.

'A phone call?'

'Sophie,' she enlightened him, her voice heavy.

The name hung between them for a second. Then Rogan shrugged. 'So?'

'So you led me to believe that she was in your past?'

'She is, she's an ex-girlfriend.'

'She doesn't seem to know that she's an ex.'

'Look, Laura, Sophie has nothing to do with you and me. My relationship with her ended ages ago.'

'She sounded upset.'

'What do you want me to do—go round and comfort her?'

She flinched at his cool sarcasm. What she wanted was to know that she herself meant something to him, that she wouldn't be discarded like Sophie. It was a forlorn hope and she was being ridiculous, she knew that. She also knew that the longer she pursued this particular line of conversation the sooner he would tire of her.

'You have no need to be jealous of Sophie, Laura. I can assure you of that.' He touched her face in a gentle, persuasive and compelling caress.

'I'm not jealous.' She pulled away from him.

'So what's this about, then?' he asked patiently.

She met his eyes, so dark, so seductive. This was about being in love with someone who didn't return her feelings, she thought with a sigh. It was her problem, not his. He had promised her nothing and she would have to accept the status quo or else walk away from the relationship. Walking away seemed an unendurable option. She wanted so much to be part of his life.

'Nothing,' she said in a low voice. Then she shrugged. 'It's just that she sounded so upset on the phone, and you're still wearing her watch. The affair must have been serious once.'

'It's a nice watch.' He shrugged. 'Yes, I'm not saying I wasn't fond of Sophie. We had some good times together. But then she changed and became obsessively possessive.'

'Cardinal sin,' Laura drawled sardonically.

'To be perfectly honest, I started to worry about her, Laura. I never led her on, but she refused to believe me when I told her that I didn't feel the same way she did. The affair got very claustrophobic. In the end I had to be cruel to be kind and I made a clean break with her. I really thought I was doing her a favour and that she'd be happy with someone else by now. 'I feel sorry for her, Laura, but I have moved on. She's part of my past and she's going to stay there. I never go back.'

Her eyes moved over his strong, handsome features. 'Am I part of your future?'

'You're part of my present,' he said firmly.

She smiled at that, but it was a trembling shadow of a smile. 'You don't make promises, do you, Rogan?'

His eyes moved tenderly over the porcelain paleness of her skin and the soft curve of her lips. 'Only ones I am absolutely sure I'll be able to keep.'

'And you are not absolutely sure about me?'

'I'm absolutely sure that I want you in my bed.' He smiled at her. 'I've been wanting you all day.'

She wanted him as well. But it wasn't enough. The ache inside her wouldn't be satisfied just with having his body—she wanted him totally. She almost laughed aloud at her own foolishness.

He reached out and covered her hand with his. 'OK?'

She said nothing but she knew it would have to be— for now.

'Shall we go back to the apartment?' His voice was husky and her body heated instantly. She hated herself for the weakness he could stir up inside her with no effort at all.

'Shouldn't you see your sister before you go back to Dublin?' she asked him, forcing herself to ignore the demands of her body.

'I called her from the office. We're not going to have time.'

'Fine.' Laura forced herself to sound unconcerned, but the fact that he hadn't introduced her to his sister seemed to speak volumes. It proved that he wasn't serious about her.

She slid the box with the necklace in it back across the table towards him. 'I can't accept such an expensive gift, Rogan, but thank you anyway.'

'Why?' He stared at her. 'I want you to have it.'

She shook her head. 'It would just make me feel beholden to you.'

'I don't mind,' he assured her with a return of that amused tone in his voice.

'I do.' She kept her voice calm and rational. 'If I took it I would only feel guilty.'

'Guilty about what?'

'Seeing someone else, of course.'

'What the hell are you talking about?' He sounded really irritated now and a few people at surrounding tables glanced over at them.

Laura suppressed a smile. Maybe she was being childish, but she wanted him to feel as uncertain about her as he made her feel about him. Perhaps if she played him at his own game, kept herself slightly aloof, she would have more chance of pulling him closer than if she were to turn possessive. It was worth a try—anything was worth trying.

'We may as well be adult about this.' She reached out and touched his hand in the same way he had hers a few moments ago. 'You are not the only one who doesn't want to make commitments—who wants a no-strings affair,' she said simply. 'And I just don't feel right about accepting such an expensive gift. OK?'

He stared at her. It was clear that he was used to calling the shots in a relationship and this turn-about frankly astonished him. 'You are one unpredictable woman, Laura Taylor,' he said, with a shake of his head. 'Obstreperous, too.'

'I'll take that as a compliment, shall I?'

'Take it any way you want.' He put the box with the

necklace back in his pocket. 'Shall we go back to my apartment?' He looked at her with a raised eyebrow.

The seductive gleam in his eye reminded her sharply that she wasn't as in control as she had tried to sound. 'If you want.' She tried very hard to appear indifferent.

'I do want, very much.' The come-hither tone made her last vestige of self-control melt.

She looked across and met his eyes. 'Shall we call a cab?'

CHAPTER ELEVEN

ROGAN was alone in bed when he woke up the next morning. He stretched and sat up, wondering where Laura was.

Then the bedroom door opened and she came in. He was surprised to see she was fully dressed. She looked well groomed and confident in a black trouser suit and white silk blouse. Her hair, softly shining, was gathered back from her face and fastened with a silver clasp.

'What time is it?' he asked with a frown.

'Seven o'clock.' She put a cup of tea on his bedside table for him.

'You had me worried. For a moment I thought it was later. How come you are up and dressed so early?'

'This is my usual time for getting up.' She was going around the bedroom, picking up items that belonged to her—a pair of shoes from beside the bed, a dressing-gown on the chair. 'I thought I may as well pack and be ready to leave.'

'But we don't have to go for a good few hours.' He stretched out and caught her arm as she passed close by him. 'We have plenty of time to play before we pack.'

The note of desire in his voice nearly tempted her to sit next to him on the bed. It was only with a supreme effort that she made herself pull away from him. 'I think we've had our play time,' she said briskly. 'I want to run my eye over those designs and phone through to your office, make sure Helen and I are in complete agreement with the final plans.'

'Helen?' He frowned. 'Who—?'

'Your chief window-dresser at the store on Fifth.'
Laura turned and left the room.

With a sigh Rogan got out of bed. He didn't want to
talk about business, he wanted Laura back in bed, but
as she seemed to have other plans he would have to go
along with it.

Laura threw the last of her belongings in her case and
stared out of the window at the Manhattan skyline. It
had taken every scrap of her will-power to walk out of
that bedroom, but she sensed that if she were to have
any kind of relationship with Rogan she'd have to try
much harder to be something she wasn't. Controlled,
casual. Act like her affair with him was secondary to her
work.

She heard the hiss of the shower in the bathroom.
Rogan would be out in a little while and she would take
it from there.

She walked across to the telephone and called the office on Fifth.

She was still talking about the plans for the Celtic
designs when Rogan emerged from the bedroom, fully
dressed.

'You think so?' Laura was saying. 'OK, well, I'll fax
the details to you when I get back to the Dublin office.'
She smiled indifferently at Rogan, as if he were someone
who had just walked into her office and was waiting for
an appointment.

'OK, thanks, Helen. I'll speak to you later.' She put
down the phone and turned to Rogan. 'Listen, I've had
a wonderful idea,' she said brightly. 'Why don't we use
pictures of the Fitzroy castle to publicise the Celtic
range?'

Rogan nodded, his eyes moving over her slowly. She
looked gorgeous. Her eyes were shining with enthusiasm, her hand on her hip pushing her jacket back slightly
to reveal the soft curves of her figure. He felt a longing
well up inside.

'Rogan, are you listening to me?' she asked with a tinge of impatience.

'Sure, sounds like a good idea.' He reached out and pulled her into his arms.

For a while she allowed him to kiss her. The warmth of his lips almost made her forget what she was doing. The heady sensuality that flowed between them too strong to pull away from.

It was with a supreme effort that she put a hand against his chest and gently levered herself away from him.

'So shall I put the plan into action when we get back to Dublin? The castle is a very dramatic, romantic image. I'm sure Lord Fitzroy would be thrilled.'

She felt a little surge of pleasure at the momentary gleam of annoyance that lit Rogan's dark eyes. 'Can't we talk about this later, on the plane? We've got two hours to spare before we have to leave. I thought we could use it for pleasure.'

She felt herself weakening. 'If that's what you want...'

The ringing of the phone interrupted them. Laura pulled away from him. 'That will be Helen. She said she'd phone me back.'

Rogan stretched across her and lifted the receiver. 'I'll deal with this,' he said firmly.

A second later the tone of his voice changed, became softer and more indulgent. 'Don't worry. As it turns out, I do have some time. I'll come over and see what I can do.'

'Problems?' Laura asked as he put the phone down.

Rogan grinned at her. 'A crisis at my sister's house. Her washing-machine has packed in and the repair man can't come until tomorrow.'

'Now that is a crisis,' Laura agreed with a smile.

'I guess pleasure will have to wait.' Rogan pulled her towards him and kissed her gently on the lips. 'I'll have

to go around and see if I can do anything. Would you
like to come?'

She laughed. 'You know very well that I would.'

Sarah lived in a large brownstone family home not far
from Rogan's apartment.

Laura liked her immediately. She also liked the warm,
friendly atmosphere in the house. Totally unlike the ster-
ile atmosphere of Rogan's apartment, it was filled with
books and children's toys and vases of fresh flowers. The
lounge with its squashy sofas looked lived-in and
slightly untidy.

'Rogan, thanks for coming over,' Sarah murmured as
she embraced her brother. 'And, Laura, I'm very pleased
to meet you,' she said sincerely. 'Sorry to get you over
here under these circumstances, but I can't cope without
that machine.'

Rogan laughed. 'I know. I'll go down to the basement
and see what I can do.'

'Can you stay for lunch?'

'No time, Sarah. We can only have a quick coffee
now,' Rogan said.

Sarah rolled her eyes. 'You never have any time,' she
complained with a smile.

Rogan was waylaid on the way downstairs by Sarah's
twins, two four-year-old girls who flung themselves on
him with squeals of delight.

'Come through to the kitchen, Laura.'

Following Sarah further through the house and into
the kitchen, Laura was struck by how like her brother
she was. She had the same dark hair and dark eyes but,
whereas Rogan was tall and broad, she was petite and
very feminine.

'Rogan's good with children, isn't he?' Laura remarked casually as the laughter increased in the hallway
and Rogan's teasing voice drifted through.

'Yes, he is. It's a pity he hasn't had any of his own.'

Sarah sighed. 'But, then, you probably know my feelings on that score.'

'Rogan has mentioned you keep trying to marry him off.'

'In a subtle way,' Sarah said.

The women's eyes met and they both laughed.

'Rogan hates it whenever I even mention the M word.' Sarah put some china beakers on a tray.

'I suppose he's had a bad experience of marriage and doesn't want to make another mistake.'

For a moment Sarah regarded her steadily. 'You're right. He did have a particularly tough time of it with Melony. She never loved him. All she was interested in was his money.'

'Poor Rogan,' Laura murmured. 'He hasn't really talked a lot about his ex-wife. It's no wonder.'

'Her affair came as a terrible blow for him. Rogan thought he was building the business up so that they could have a good standard of living, I think he was even keen on starting a family. Then he discovered that Mel was only interested in the almighty dollar…and had no intention of starting a family at all. The only thing she was interested in starting was an affair with Rogan's so-called best friend. She's a very mercenary, very cool customer.'

'It's no wonder that he's wary of commitment,' Laura said sadly.

'The fact that our parents divorced when we were both young hasn't helped.' Sarah pulled a face as she heard her brother's footsteps, coming towards them from the hall. 'For heaven's sake, don't tell Rogan I've been discussing him like this. He'll be mad with me. He thinks I dabble too much in his personal matters as it is.' She smiled at Laura. 'But we women have these things to do, don't we?'

'Certainly,' Laura agreed wryly.

'And, anyway, you've filled me with new hope,'

Sarah said suddenly. 'You are the only girlfriend Rogan has talked to me about in a long time—without my having to twist his arm, that is. He's told me about your daughter who's nearly thirteen and your son... Matthew?'

'That's right.' Laura felt a jolt of surprise and pleasure at this revelation.

'He thinks they are wonderful children.'

'They are but, then, of course, I am biased.'

The door opened and Rogan joined them. He had a little girl tucked under each arm. 'I think I'll have to leave these two in here with you,' he said with a grin, 'otherwise this machine will never be repaired.'

Sarah reached to take the children. 'By the way,' she said, giving him a wide, innocent smile, 'I'm planning a dinner for Thanksgiving. Do you think you and Laura might be able to come? You could bring Laura's children.'

'Sarah, I don't think there is any way we will make Thanksgiving dinner, but thanks, anyway. You are forgetting one little thing. Laura and the children live a continent away.'

Sarah shrugged. 'I've never been one to let little things stand in my way.'

The darkened streets of Dublin glistened from an earlier downpour, the streetlights reflecting in orange pools of light in the puddles. Laura couldn't help thinking how small everything looked after New York, how provincial.

Rogan turned the car away from the city and drove out towards her cottage. The only sound was the swish of the tyres on the wet surface of the road.

The flight home had seemed longer and more arduous than the one going out, perhaps because they were both tired.

Rogan had worked almost continuously throughout

the flight and she had helped out with some of the papers, before finally drifting into a deep uncomfortable sleep for the last hour of the journey.

She felt tired now, but she was excited at the prospect of seeing the children—of wrapping her arms around them and hearing their excited chatter. She'd missed them. Glancing at her watch, she noticed it was past their bedtime, but with a bit of luck Cora would have let them stay up and wait for her.

For a moment she remembered her pleasure at hearing Sarah tell her that Rogan had spoken about her children, a pleasure which had been quickly swept away at Rogan's curt yet practical reminder later that they lived a continent apart.

Of course they did. Rogan's home was that apartment in New York and her place was here. She had allowed herself to forget that stark truth. All her plans for playing things cool and her hopes for drawing Rogan closer were quite absurd. Rogan was American and she was Irish. The fact that he had a house here didn't mean that much. Hadn't he said himself that it was a second home, that his main business and his life lay in America?

It started to rain again as he turned the car into her driveway. The headlights lit the tangled, overgrown garden, highlighting the silver drops of rain which seemed to hang in suspended animation from the tangled chaos of jasmine and ivy.

The front door opened as soon as they pulled to a halt.

Laura's emotions soared as she saw Joanne and Matthew silhouetted against the warm light from within.

She reached for the doorhandle and dashed through the rain towards the cottage, taking them both into her arms and holding them close.

'Did you have a good time? Was it wonderful?' Joanne asked excitedly.

Before she had a chance to answer Rogan came in behind her with her suitcase.

'Rogan! Rogan!' Matthew ran to him and the next moment he was being lifted and swung in strong arms.

'Good to see you,' Rogan said, as he put him down and ruffled the dark hair.

Joanne also went over to greet him.

The strength of the welcome the children gave Rogan startled Laura.

Cora came out into the hall. 'How was New York?' she asked, kissing Laura on the cheek.

'We didn't have much time for sightseeing, but it's a great city.'

'Even less time, with my sister dragging us around to her house,' Rogan said, a hint of amusement in his tone as he looked over at Laura.

'Come on in and get warmed by the fire. I've just boiled the kettle,' Cora said, leading the way into the lounge.

For a while they sat, talking about the trip. Laura was asked about the flight, the type of plane, the shops and Rogan's apartment. There were shouts of delight as she got out the gifts she had bought.

Then Cora got up to go home. 'Thank you so much, Mum,' Laura said, walking with her to the front door. 'Were the children good?'

'Of course they were good.' Cora grinned. 'We've enjoyed ourselves. By the way—' she dropped her voice to a low whisper '—I didn't have a chance to tell you before you went away, but I think Rogan is gorgeous.'

'So do I.' Laura smiled. 'But the relationship isn't going anywhere, Mum, so don't start dropping hints, will you?'

'You are such a spoilsport.' Cora's eyes were teasing. 'I'm free to babysit for you tomorrow night before you ask.'

'Tomorrow?'

'Robert's leaving party, isn't it?' Cora reminded her.

'Oh, yes.' Laura nodded. 'Are you sure?'

'Course I'm sure. Goodnight, darling.'

As Laura returned to the lounge she remembered she was supposed to be attending that party with Paul. She wondered if Rogan would want to take her.

Matthew was sitting next to Rogan on the settee. Laura noticed he was listening with an enraptured expression on his young face as Rogan answered more questions from Joanne about New York.

'Are you going to marry my mum?' he asked suddenly and very solemnly when there was a gap in the conversation.

Joanne's face went red with embarrassment. Laura nearly fell over the dog. Only Rogan seemed unfazed. 'Your mother and I are very good friends,' he answered, without the slightest flicker of awkwardness. 'Is that all right?'

Matthew nodded. 'It would be all right if you got married, too. I wouldn't mind, neither would Joanne. We talked about it yesterday.'

'Matthew!' Joanne wailed, her cheeks going even redder.

Rogan laughed.

'Now, come on, you two, enough of this nonsense.' Laura cut across the proceedings quickly, her voice brisk. 'It's time for bed.'

They both rose immediately, Joanne looking as if she would be glad to get out of the room and Matthew innocently unabashed.

Laura could hear them arguing as they went up the stairs. 'I told you not to ask him that,' Joanne was saying in a low, angry tone.

'Sorry about that,' Laura said looking over at Rogan.

'That's OK.' He seemed amused.

There was a moment's silence, filled only by the soft crackle of the fire.

'I suppose you are tired and you'll want to get home,' she said.

'I'm ready for bed, but I don't know about the second part of that question,' he drawled. 'I was hoping you might ask me to stay, and we could make up for the time we missed together in New York.'

She felt the heat of longing steal through her body, surreptitiously countering her questions and doubts about where this relationship could lead.

'You know, I've never had a casual affair before,' she said hesitantly. 'I'm not sure of the ground rules.'

'I'm making the rules up as I go along, as far as you and I are concerned. Hadn't you noticed?' he said teasingly.

'I'm not sure if I should let you stay here,' she said quietly.

One eyebrow rose at that. 'Why not?'

'Because it might confuse the children. They already seem to be thinking along the wrong lines. I don't want them to be hurt.' She put into words the niggle of fear she had felt since seeing how delighted the children had been to welcome Rogan back.

He frowned and seemed to be seriously considering her words. 'Maybe you're right,' he said slowly. 'The last thing I want is to upset the children.'

'Mum.' Matthew's voice drifted downstairs. 'Mum, are you going to tuck me in?'

'Coming.' Laura looked over at Rogan. 'I won't be a moment.'

By the time Laura had tucked Matthew in and kissed him, he was already asleep. Obviously the excitement and the late night was taking its toll. Laura switched off his lamp and closed the door of his room quietly, before going down to the end of the corridor to check if Joanne was all right.

She was surprised to see that she, too, was fast asleep, her long hair spread over the pink covers in a mane of

gold and her cheeks faintly flushed with healthy colour.
Laura kissed her and switched off the light.

When she went back downstairs Rogan was standing
in the lounge.

'Are they OK?'

She nodded. 'They are both fast asleep. Would you
like another drink?' There was a part of her that didn't
want him to go, couldn't bear to say goodbye. To sleep
alone in her bed, after the warmth of sharing a bed with
him, was a very unwelcome thought.

Rogan seemed to think about the invitation.

'If you're tired—' she began.

'Surprisingly enough, I'm not tired,' he interrupted. 'I
was trying to be sensible, but I find that's very difficult
around you. I understand what you said about the children and giving them the wrong idea, but I find myself
thinking that if they are asleep do they need to know
that I've stayed?'

Laura didn't answer him immediately and he came
over to her and kissed her.

'I'll leave very early before they wake up,' he whispered against her ear, before kissing her again.

The heat of his kiss melted her resistance and her
heart.

She found herself wrapping her arms around his neck
as he picked her up to carry her upstairs.

Rogan lay, staring up at the ceiling and listening to the
heavy lashing of the early morning rain. They had come
to bed in such a hurry last night that the curtains weren't
properly drawn. As the dawn light stole into the room
he could see a triangle of light on the ceiling. The reflection of the water, running down the window-panes
in seemingly never-ending rivulets, gave the effect of
tears over the white ceiling.

He could hear Laura's steady breathing next to him
and feel the warmth and the softness of her skin.

He wanted her again. He never seemed to be able to get enough of her. But he was thinking about what she had said about the children and remembering Matthew's words and the way the little boy had greeted him with such unreserved pleasure last night.

Rogan had meant it when he had said that the very last thing he wanted was to hurt the children. He was very fond of them—in fact, he was surprised by the strength of his feelings for them in such a short space of time. Maybe it was because he sensed a certain vulnerability in them. They both missed a father figure in their life. Matthew, especially, seemed to look at him with a kind of expectancy—a kind of hope—that tore at him. He knew what it was like to miss a parent.

Laura was right. They shouldn't give them false expectations. He rolled over and looked at the clock on the bedside table. Then his eyes moved to Laura's sleeping form. She was beautiful.

She opened her eyes as if she sensed him watching her. He leaned over and kissed her gently on the lips.

'What time is it?' she murmured sleepily, moving a little closer to him.

For a moment he allowed his hand to curve around her waist and stroke her silky skin. Then he pressed a kiss against her cheek. 'Time I was going.'

She rolled over and watched as he pulled back the covers and swung out of bed.

'Rogan?'

'Mmm?' He didn't glance at her. He was busy buttoning up his shirt.

'It's the leaving party for Robert tonight.' She sat up and pushed a hand through her hair.

'Yes, I know.'

She waited to see if he would say he'd pick her up or even ask if she would accompany him. He said nothing more.

'Paul asked if I'd go with him. I was wondering—'

'Good idea.' He cut across her briskly. 'We can't very well turn up together at a business party. It would set people talking. Far better if we turn up separately.'

'So, if Paul accompanies me who will you go with?'

'A partner isn't a problem, Laura.'

Laura felt as if he had just hit her.

He was now dressed and obviously anxious to leave without further discussion. He picked up his jacket from the chair. 'See you at the office.' He bent to kiss her and she had to force herself not to turn away.

'See you at the office,' she murmured as the door closed behind him.

CHAPTER TWELVE

LAURA stood at the bedroom window of her cottage that evening. Heavy rain battered the pane of glass, almost obliterating the path which was lit by the outdoor light.

The wind was getting up. It howled and whooshed over the small house in an eerie way. It wasn't a night for going out but a night for curling up in front of the fire...preferably with Rogan.

She sighed and turned to look at her reflection in the cheval mirror. There was no chance of staying in, and certainly not with Rogan.

She was going to Robert's party tonight with Paul. And Rogan would probably be there with another woman.

Thinking about that made her heart thud unevenly. Was it only this morning that he had been in her bed, holding her and kissing her? She had tried not to be angry about his suggestion that they should attend tonight's function with different partners but inside she was still raw about it.

She supposed he was right. If they arrived together and left together people would talk.

Things would be a lot simpler if she wasn't in love with him, Laura decided, if she could just enjoy having an affair with him without the intensity of emotions which were tearing her apart.

But that wasn't her style. She didn't seem capable of giving her body without giving her heart. She ran a smoothing hand down over the figure-hugging red dress.

She heard a car pull up outside and picked up her wrap and her handbag to go downstairs.

The children were in the lounge, and Cora had gone to open the front door. Laura could hear her voice warm with welcome as she talked to Paul.

She went into the hall to join them. Paul looked very suave in a dark dinner suit, his blond hair groomed neatly into place with the aid of styling gel.

'Laura, you look lovely,' he said, his eyes sweeping admiringly over her slender figure.

'Thank you, Paul,' she said, averting her cheek as he bent to kiss her. She turned and saw Matthew and Joanne, watching them from the doorway of the lounge.

She was aware that the children were not pleased that she wasn't going to the party with Rogan. Both had expressed dismay and then annoyance when Laura had tried to explain, by saying very simply that Rogan was just a friend and her boss. She had tried to act as if there had never been any question that they would be attending the party as a couple.

'You remember Joanne and Matt, don't you, Paul?' she said in an attempt to draw the children out of the sullen way they were regarding them both.

'Yes, of course I do. Hi, there, kids,' Paul said in a bright but rather insincere tone. 'Haven't seen you for a while.'

'Hello.' The reply from both children was flat.

'How's school?' Paul made a more determined effort to get a response.

'OK.' Joanne was the only one to answer, her curt reply filled with hostility. Then they both turned and went back into the lounge.

'I won't be a minute, Paul,' Laura said, and followed the children, closing the door behind her and leaving her mother to entertain the visitor for a moment.

'OK, you two, you were a bit abrupt with poor old Paul, you know,' she said gently. 'He didn't deserve such a welcome.' She sat next to Matthew on the couch. 'What's the matter?'

'You know what the matter is,' Matthew mumbled. 'You should be going to the party with Rogan.'

'You are being very silly, you know.' Laura strove to find the right things to say to make them feel better. The trouble was she felt low herself. It wasn't what she wanted either.

'It's all Matthew's fault,' Joanne said crossly. 'If he hadn't said what he did Rogan would be here now. Matt scared him away with that marriage talk.'

'Oh, that's rubbish, Jo, and you know it.' Laura put her arm around Matthew and pulled him close to give him a cuddle.

'Rogan and I are still very good friends and nothing you have said or done has influenced anything... honestly.'

Laura looked over at her daughter. 'Come and give me a hug and tell me you love me and let's forget this silliness.'

Joanne didn't move immediately, then she got up grudgingly. 'I'm a bit old for giving hugs,' she murmured, then grinned as she caught the look of horror on her mother's face.

'You're never too old to hug.' Laura put her arm around both children and drew them close against her, drawing strength from their love. 'You know, we have got each other and that's what really counts. Now, how about us going to the theatre tomorrow night? I think *Riverdance* is on. What do you say?'

'Is Rogan going to come?' Matthew asked.

'No, just the three of us. The three musketeers.'

'The three musketeers were men,' Joanne muttered.

'What do you say? Shall I try and get tickets?'

'OK.' Joanne shrugged.

'That's not the response I want.' Laura tickled them both so that they started to giggle. 'I want shrieks of excited enthusiasm.' She kept tickling them until they rolled to the floor with laughter.

'Great, great,' Joanne gasped. 'The theatre will be wonderful.'

'That's better. Now, come out and say goodnight to Paul and behave like the kind-hearted and polite children I know you really are.'

Jewels blazed at the throats of fashionably dressed women and the men all wore dark dinner suits. A band played and the dance floor was almost as packed as the sides of the room.

Laura took a glass of orange juice from the tray of a passing waiter, and as she did so she saw Rogan. His height and bearing made him stand out from every other man. There was something about him, something that exuded power and confidence and magnetic attraction.

He was surrounded by people, one of them a glamorous blonde. Her hair was piled on top of her head in a sleek style and her curvaceous figure was shown to its best advantage in a glittering gown of gold which was low and plunging at the back—and the front.

Rogan threw back his head and laughed at something she had said.

Laura's body responded with a violent thrust of emotion. She wanted Rogan so much. It was like a form of torture, seeing him with someone else.

She was going to have to pull herself together, she told herself. It had been difficult enough to cope with the children's disappointment without this emotional turmoil, tearing her apart. She needed to compose herself.

She sipped at her drink, looked around in the opposite direction from her boss and tried to concentrate on Paul's conversation.

She saw Robert James, making his way across the room towards them.

'Laura, how nice to see you.' His face was wreathed in a smile of pleasure.

'How are things, Robert?' she asked, kissing him on the cheek. 'Are you enjoying your retirement?'

'Oh, I'm getting by.' Although there was humour in his tone, Laura thought she detected a certain sadness as well.

'You've certainly got a good turn-out tonight,' she said brightly. 'It's a tremendous accolade to your business achievements.'

'Yes, I suppose it is.' He nodded. 'It's nice to see everyone again. Tell me, how are things going at the office?'

They talked for a while about business and then, when someone else claimed his attention, Paul asked if she would like to dance. They made their way to the crowded dance floor.

'Robert hasn't quite reconciled himself to retirement,' Paul said, taking her into his arms and bending to speak in a low tone against her ear.

'It will take a while, I suppose. James Design has been such a large part of his life.'

As they turned in time to the slow music she saw Rogan.

He was standing at the other side of the room, still surrounded by the same crowd of people, with the same woman by his side.

He looked directly over at her and she looked hurriedly away, but she was aware of his eyes, resting contemplatively on her.

She smiled up at Paul. 'How are things with you, anyway? It seems ages since we went out together.'

'It is ages.' Paul sounded glum.

Something about his tone made her frown. 'Are you all right, Paul? You sound...I don't know...different somehow.'

Paul shrugged. 'If I'm honest, I suppose I'm jealous.'

'Jealous?'

'You and Rogan Powers. Your mother mentioned that

you were in New York with him when I phoned you this week.'

'It was just business.' Laura looked away from him, feeling uncomfortable about lying. 'Anyway, you and I have always just been friends, Paul. You've had your girlfriends, and I've been out with other men—'

'I know, but somehow I feel Rogan is different. It made me start to think about things between you and me.' He put a hand under her chin, forcing her to look up into his eyes. 'Laura, I want you,' he said softly. 'Listen, how about you and I going out for something to eat tomorrow night?'

'I hate to interrupt such a touching scene but I wondered if I might have this dance?'

Rogan's deep voice from behind them sent Laura's emotions into a spin. Somehow she forced herself to turn and meet his eyes with cool composure.

'Good evening, Rogan.' She managed a smile and was quite proud of herself.

His eyes moved over her figure. Her dress was simple yet elegant, the soft silk emphasising her womanly curves and the dramatic colour a vibrant contrast to the darkness of her hair and pale smoothness of her skin.

Then Rogan's gaze moved to Paul in a swift assessing look, taking in the possessive arm that he still had around Laura's waist.

'You don't mind, Paul?' he asked.

'Well...no...' Paul didn't look too pleased as Rogan reached out to take Laura by the hand.

Laura felt torn. She wanted to be with Rogan but she hated to think Paul was upset. She didn't want to hurt him, though she'd been quite shocked by his words.

Paul made the decision for her, turning quickly to leave them.

Her heart felt as if it was pumping overtime as she stepped into Rogan's arms.

The scent of his cologne and the way he held her close

to his body reminded her of that night in New York when they had dined together and then made love afterwards.

She tried to close her mind to those memories. She felt hurt that he had brought another woman with him tonight. She supposed dully that, like Paul, she was jealous. It was an emotion alien to her and she didn't like it one little bit.

She angled her chin and met his eyes. 'Aren't you afraid that people might talk if they see us dancing together?' she asked him coolly. 'It could cause quite a scandal, I'm sure.'

'I've decided to weather the storm.'

His dry amusement angered her. OK, he probably had a point. If they had come here tonight as a couple there would have been gossip. She tried to reason with herself so that she wouldn't say anything she might regret.

'Very brave of you.' She gave a small laugh. She didn't feel like laughing. Strangely, she sounded as if she couldn't care less.

'You seem to have been enjoying yourself with Paul,' Rogan remarked.

'He's a terrific guy.' She looked up at him and felt a sense of exhilaration when she saw the flicker of annoyance in his dark eyes. 'But, then, I've always had a soft spot for Paul.'

'Is that so? I thought you said he was just a friend and nothing more.'

'Like you and I.' She smiled airily. Let him make what he wanted of that, she thought. 'Actually, he was just asking me out to dinner when you interrupted us.'

'Was he, indeed?' Now Rogan sounded totally unconcerned. 'By all means, don't let me stand in your way if you want to accept.'

Her small sense of power, of wanting to hurt him the way he had hurt her, was extinguished like a candle by a fire extinguisher.

'You don't mind, then?' She tilted her chin to look at him again.

'I have no real right to mind, do I?' he drawled. 'Not when I told you that you should come here with him tonight.'

'I suppose not.' She looked away from his eyes.

'Who is the woman with you?' She hated herself for asking. She didn't want him to guess at the depth of the jealousy she felt.

'Which woman?'

Laura felt a stab of annoyance. 'The one with the blonde hair and gold dress.'

'Jennifer Kelly. She's the daughter of a business associate.'

'She's beautiful.'

'She's only eighteen.'

Old enough for an affair, Laura thought dryly. 'Well, you know what they say—variety is the spice of life,' she said lightly.

She looked up at him, and suddenly found herself saying something she hadn't planned at all. 'You know, Rogan, I think I will accept Paul's invitation to dinner. I hope you won't be too cross with me but I think we should call a halt to our...association. I've got the children to think of and, really, if I'm going to get involved with anyone for any length of time it's got to be a steady, reliable relationship.'

The music came to an end and she took the opportunity to pull away from him. 'Thanks for the dance, Rogan.' She smiled up at him, her manner very cool yet dignified at the same time.

He didn't answer her. He was stunned, and yet she had only done what he himself had been thinking of doing since their return from New York.

As she walked away from him his hands tightened into clenched fists at his side. He wanted to run after her, run after her and say... What the hell would he say?

he asked himself, and raked an impatient hand through his hair. Instead, he moved across to where Jennifer stood patiently, waiting for him.

Robert James stopped him on the way across. 'Lovely girl, isn't she?' he said to Rogan with a nod in Laura's direction.

'Yes...lovely.' Rogan agreed. He found he wasn't much in the mood for small talk.

'I'm hoping that Paul will have the good sense to propose to her,' Robert said idly. 'I've always thought Laura would make the perfect daughter-in-law.'

Rogan frowned and looked at Robert, as if seeing him for the first time.

The music was dying down and someone was getting onto the stage at the far end of the room, calling for Robert to come up and speak to everyone.

Thunderous applause filled the ballroom. It seemed to echo hollowly through Rogan's very soul. Everyone's eyes were on Robert as he went up to the front of the room, but Rogan's attention was firmly centred on where Laura stood with Paul.

CHAPTER THIRTEEN

LAURA closed the front door quietly. She was relieved to be home, away from the noise and the cheerful atmosphere of the party. She didn't feel cheerful. She felt like crying.

Paul had been disappointed not to be asked in and despondent when he couldn't change her mind about going out with him. She'd noticed when she'd told him she was going to the theatre tomorrow night with the children that he hadn't asked if he could come with them. Rogan would have done.

The thought was unwelcome. It was over between her and Rogan. She leaned against the door and tried to gather her thoughts, before going through to her mother.

She hadn't intended to call everything off with Rogan, but it had been the right thing to do. She had been naïve in the extreme to think she could handle an affair with him. Just seeing him talking to another woman had cut her in two.

Taking a deep breath, Laura went into the lounge.

The television was on, with the volume turned low. Her mother was sitting in the chair next to the fire, with Captain asleep at her feet.

'Had a nice time?'

'It was pleasant,' Laura lied. 'Were the children good?'

'A bit subdued,' Cora admitted, 'but they were all right by bedtime.'

Laura looked over at her mother. She was struck by how lovely she looked. Her hair was a very light blonde, its short layers framing a face that had classical features.

'So, what's the problem between you and Rogan Powers?' she asked gently.

'Did the children say something about him?'

'They didn't have to. You all look as if you've lost your best friend.'

Laura had to smile at that. Her mother had always been there for her in good times and bad. She was nothing if not perceptive. 'I'm in love with him,' she admitted huskily.

'Good.' Her mother smiled. 'It's about time you risked giving your heart again. You are too young to be shut away from life.'

'I'm not shut away from life, Mum,' Laura said patiently.

'You are afraid of getting hurt again,' Cora said decisively. 'I don't blame you, Laura, you've been through a tough time. But that's in the past. You should enjoy yourself now.'

'I agree with you and I might just be tempted to throw caution away and have a fling with Rogan except that I've got to consider the children.' She sighed. 'They are getting far too fond of him, Mum. If I allow him into their lives any further they'll be devastated when the relationship ends. I can't risk that. They've been through enough, losing their father.'

There was silence for a moment. 'They do like him a lot.'

Laura nodded. 'I've done the only thing I can do. I've told Rogan we can't see each other socially again.'

Cora frowned. 'But isn't that running away? You don't know the relationship would have ended—'

'I do,' Laura said firmly. 'I've got to be realistic. Rogan isn't one for long-term commitments. Then there's the problem that he lives in the States...' She shook her head. 'I've done the right thing.' The words sounded as empty as she felt.

'He seemed to really like the children, though,' Cora said with a shake of her head.

'He's out tonight with another woman,' Laura said flatly.

'Pity, I was starting to think you might get married again.'

'Married?' Laura looked at her mother, shocked.

'Isn't that what you wanted?' Cora asked calmly.

'No.' Laura's eyes widened. 'I'll never get married again. I…just wanted a steady relationship.'

'In my day that was called marriage,' Cora said dryly.

Laura had waited all Monday morning for a glimpse of Rogan, but she didn't see him. Her disappointment was acute. She didn't know what she had expected today, but it wasn't his silence.

It was Paul who strolled into Laura's office early in the afternoon.

'Hello.' Laura looked up at him in surprise. 'I thought you were supposed to be taking things easy now that you're a director here.' Her voice was light and jovial.

'I can't keep away from you,' Paul murmured, but there was a return of the teasing glint in his eye and his good-natured grin. 'I'm not going to give up, you know, not until you tell me you'll come out for dinner.'

'Paul, I explained on Friday night—'

'Is this a meeting-house or a place of work?' The sarcastic voice cut across Laura's words, taking both of them by surprise.

Laura looked up and her temperature soared as she met Rogan's eyes. Of all the times for him to choose to come and see her… Why did he have to come now?

'Sorry, Rogan.' Paul turned, his manner one of easy charm. 'I was on my way up to Accounts with those figures we discussed the other day and I got waylaid. I just had to have a minute with Laura.'

'Really.' Rogan's tone was flat. 'Don't let me detain

you with those figures, then.' He nodded at the file Paul had put down.

'No…right.' Paul flashed a rather puzzled look at Laura. 'We'll arrange dinner later,' he said firmly, before heading for the door.

Laura couldn't wait for Paul to go. She felt as if Rogan's eyes were cutting into her. As the door closed, the atmosphere in the office was electric.

'What can I do for you, Rogan?' she asked, her manner businesslike. She glanced down at the work on her desk, pretending an indifference to him she just didn't feel.

He didn't answer, and when the silence grew longer she was forced to look up at him. He looked great, she thought, her heart twisting. He was wearing a dark blue suit, the white of his shirt contrasting with the darkness of his hair and eyes. She was so much in love with him that it hurt.

She looked away again at the drawing board in front of her. She wondered if he had started an affair with that woman he'd brought to the party on Friday night. All weekend that notion had tormented her.

'Will you come and have lunch with me?' Rogan asked suddenly.

She shook her head. 'I'm busy.' It took all her willpower to turn down the invitation, all her stamina to be able to look up at him again. 'Besides, we don't have anything to say to each other, do we?'

His eyes moved contemplatively over her. 'You are not in love with Paul James,' he told her decisively.

'What would you know about love?' Laura was stung to retort sharply.

'Not much,' Rogan admitted, his tone suddenly gentle. 'I do know that marrying the wrong person can make your life hell.'

'Who's talking about marriage?' Laura frowned.

'Robert James seems to have the idea that Paul is serious about you…that it will lead to marriage.'

'Really?' Laura's eyes widened at that. Then she shrugged. 'My mother had the same idea about us.'

She watched the look of surprise on his face and her lips twitched. 'Yes, the idea shocked me as well. Robert was wrong about Paul and I…and my mother certainly got it wrong. I have no interest in getting married again.'

The silence between them was very strained for a moment. Then Laura added, 'I will continue to see Paul, though.'

'But you won't continue your relationship with me,' Rogan said suddenly in a grating voice, raking a hand through his hair. 'Hell, Laura, I don't understand you. I mean, up to a few nights ago you were making love with me.'

'I beg your pardon?' She glared up at him.

'You heard what I said. You are running away.'

She shook her head. 'Now that's something you *do* know about.' Her voice dripped with sarcasm. 'You are so frightened of commitment that you almost run backwards when you hear the word. You talk about claustrophobic relationships when someone gets too close. Of no-strings affairs and casual sex.' All pretence at civility was thrown aside as her temper suddenly flared.

'I've never talked about casual sex,' he muttered furiously.

'No, you've just "practised" that one.' Laura's tone shook with anger. 'Well, I'm not like you, Rogan. I understand you, I even sympathise with the fact that you are determined not to get hurt again.' She started to gather up the papers on her desk. 'But you don't have a monopoly on being hurt.' She swept the papers into her briefcase. 'My husband was unfaithful to me. It caused me a lot of pain…but I haven't given up on relationships because of one bad experience.'

He stared at her and frowned. 'You never told me that before.'

'Some things are too painful to discuss. I was dev-astated, Rogan, when I found out. Apparently, he had been lying and cheating on me for years and, naïve fool that I was, I never guessed a thing. An experience like that makes you very, very careful about who you choose to give your heart to.'

For the first time in Rogan's life he was totally at a loss.

She stood. 'Now, if you'll excuse me, I've got an appointment with a client.'

'No, I won't excuse you.' He caught her arm as she made to walk past him. 'I want you to answer my ques-tion. Are you in love with Paul?'

Laura stared down at the hand on her arm. 'I'd be careful, Rogan. People will talk,' she murmured. 'Re-member, people who work in glass towers shouldn't have affairs.'

'I don't give a toss who talks about what,' Rogan murmured huskily, all control gone. He pulled her closer.

The next moment she was in his arms.

'Stop it, Rogan.' Her heartbeat was out of control as she looked up at him.

'No.' He smiled suddenly as if everything in his mind was suddenly clear. 'I'm going to give this office block, this town, something to really talk about.'

She shook her head and put her hand on his shoulder to push him away.

Then he kissed her. The feeling was electric. Laura wanted to melt into his arms and never let go. Her lips met his with passion—and love.

When he let go of her she felt dazed, yet at the same time her body felt as if it were on fire.

'I don't want you to see Paul again,' Rogan murmured as he let go of her. 'I want you in my life, Laura.'

Laura stepped back from him. Her eyes moved from him through the glass walls to the rest of the office. She felt colour rising in her cheeks as she saw that everyone was watching them. As she watched, everyone stood up and started to clap. She couldn't hear it. It was like a mime—a charade, she thought angrily.

'Well, you've certainly succeeded in gaining everyone's attention,' she murmured unsteadily. Rogan looked around at the sea of faces and then grinned at her, unconcerned.

'You haven't answered me,' he said calmly.

'Well, it's quite simple. You have no right to tell me who I can and cannot see so your little piece of play-acting is of no consequence.'

'Come on, Laura, you don't really want to continue seeing Paul,' he said. 'You did it to make me jealous and it's worked. I want us to go back to the way we were—'

'I never go back.' Laura was furious now. Rogan's arrogant statement had incensed her...but she was even more angry with herself because she wanted him to kiss her again. 'Isn't that what you said to me in New York?'

'Yes but I wasn't talking about us. I—'

'You want me back because I'm the one who ended things between us, not because you're jealous,' Laura told him calmly.

For a moment he just stared at her. 'That's not true.'

'Yes, it is, hence this charade.' She gestured to indicate the office. 'You think you just have to click your fingers and you can have me back. But you can't, Rogan. I'm not playing games with you. I'm serious.'

'So am I,' Rogan said quietly.

'No, you're not,' she told him with barely concealed fury, 'otherwise you wouldn't have told me to go to that party on Friday with Paul, and you wouldn't have turned up with that...that bimbo.'

'What bimbo?' He shook his head.

'Jennifer something.'

'Oh, her! That was nothing.'

'Typical.' Laura nearly spat the word. 'The girl has my sympathy.'

The phone on the desk stared to ring but both of them ignored it. They were facing each other intently, oblivious to anything or anyone else.

'Laura, you don't understand—'

'I understand all too well. I ended our relationship on Friday night, Rogan, and I meant it.' Even as she said the words they caused a pain so deep it was almost unbearable.

The door opened and Sandra put her head around. 'I'm sorry,' she murmured apologetically as both protagonists glared at her, 'but there's an important phone call for you, Laura. It's the headmistress of the children's school.'

'What?' Laura immediately felt a wave of concern. 'Thank you, Sandra.'

She moved swiftly to pick up the receiver.

'Mrs Taylor?' The headmistress was brief. 'I'm sure it's nothing to be unduly alarmed about but I have to inform you that neither Matthew nor Joanne have returned from their lunch-break.'

'Where are they?' Laura didn't waste time on social niceties as panic rose. 'They've never skipped school before.'

'I've questioned a couple of their classmates and they said they saw the pair of them get onto a bus across the road from the school.'

Laura frowned. 'Do they know where they were going?'

'They don't seem to. I've still got them in my office and I shall question them further, but I thought you should know straight away.'

'Yes, thank you, Mrs Buckley. I'll come down to the school and see if I can find out what's happened.'

'What's wrong?' Rogan asked as she put the phone down.

She was silent for a moment as she tried to think, to get herself together. 'The children have gone missing.'

She met Rogan's eyes and was surprised and touched to see that he looked as worried as she felt.

'I'll have to go down to the school.' Her voice trembled a little. Suddenly all their arguments—everything—paled into insignificance in the worry of where the children could be.

'I'll drive you.'

For a moment Laura was going to refuse as she looked over at him.

'You're in no fit state to drive,' he said gently. 'Please let me take you.'

She nodded. She wanted him with her, she realised. She needed him.

CHAPTER FOURTEEN

THE traffic was dense. Laura was grateful that Rogan was driving. She could never have negotiated this in the state she was in.

Her mind was in turmoil as she strove to think where her children could be.

'Calm down.' Rogan's gentle voice was soothing. 'We'll find them.' He sounded quietly confident. His strength made her feel better—added calm to the chaotic jumble of her mind.

'Do you think they might have gone to your mother?' he asked.

She shook her head. 'Mum was going into town to-day.'

'Was there anything upsetting the children…worrying them?'

Laura hesitated.

Rogan stopped the car at a set of traffic lights and looked over at her. 'Whatever it was, tell me,' he urged. 'It might be something important.'

'They were upset,' she admitted huskily.

Rogan reached across and took hold of her hand, squeezing it gently. 'What about?'

She took a deep breath. 'They were upset on Friday because I went to that party with Paul instead of you.'

Rogan swore under his breath.

'I…I thought I'd cheer them up and I took them to the theatre on Saturday, but they were both very quiet…dejected.'

'Didn't they like Paul?'

'Paul didn't come.' Laura shook her head impatiently.

'It was just the three of us—the three musketeers,' she murmured, tears shimmering in her eyes. 'God, if anything happens to them I'll never forgive myself, Rogan.'

'It isn't your fault.' Rogan squeezed her hand. 'If anyone is to blame I am.'

Laura heard the note of bitter self-recrimination in his voice and turned to look at him. 'It's not your fault,' she said. 'I tried to tell them that we were just friends…tried to explain.'

'What, that I'm a fool and I don't know happiness when it hits me in the face?' Rogan said bitterly. 'How can you explain the stupidity of an adult to the simplistic, innocent mind a child has?'

Laura's heart thundered in her chest. 'They couldn't understand why we weren't together on Friday. It was such a shock to them. I couldn't understand their anger. I mean, it's not as if we'd been dating for years.'

'They sensed the magic,' Rogan said simply.

Laura looked at him with a puzzled frown.

'Come on, Laura. We both felt it. The moment my eyes met yours it was there. I was in denial, but the children recognised it for what it was.'

Laura was silent, her mind racing.

'They say that children are more attuned than adults—that they have almost a sixth sense, you know.' Rogan looked across at her. 'They knew it was right…that feeling when the four of us were together.'

Still Laura said nothing.

'I felt it—didn't you?' he persisted. 'A feeling that this was right?'

Laura tried to think rationally. 'And that's why you brought Jennifer—whatever she was called—to the party on—'

'Laura, I was wrong. I knew when I was doing it that I was wrong. The children knew—'

'Rogan, the only thing I'm interested in right now is

getting my children back,' she said abruptly. 'If anything
has happened—'

'Nothing is going to happen,' he said, his voice steady
and confident. 'I want you to think about your conversation with them on Friday. Was there any hint of what
they might be doing now in what they said?'

'No…' Laura shook her head. She could hardly think
straight she was so worried. All she knew was that she
loved her children and she didn't want them to be worried or unhappy about anything. 'Oh, Lord, what will I
do if?'

'Laura.' Rogan's voice, cool and steady, cut across
hers.

'Think about what they said—think.'

'They didn't say much.' She shook her head. 'Except…'

'Yes?'

'Well…' Laura hesitated. 'Joanne blamed Matthew
for scaring you away.' She shrugged. 'It was ridiculous
and I told them so. But both children had it in their heads
that Matt's words to you when we returned from New
York had scared you off.' Laura looked across at him.
'I told them it wasn't true.'

'Not in so many words.' Rogan's voice was grim.
'But I was scared of hurting them. I sensed…' He trailed
off. 'Laura, I have an idea,' he said suddenly.

She looked over at him, hope flaring.

'It may be nothing but…'

Suddenly Rogan was changing lanes. He drove steadily and took a left turning.

'Where are we going? I—'

'It's a chance.' He glanced over at her. 'But we are
close enough to check, without losing too much time.'

'Check what?' Her voice faded as she saw that they
were now on the road towards his house. 'You think
they might have decided they wanted to speak to you?'

'It's a long shot, but I feel we should check. They do know where my house is.'

She nodded.

'Maybe they just wanted to clear the air. See me and put their minds at rest.'

Laura's heart thudded unsteadily. She hoped and prayed he was right.

There was silence for a while as Rogan negotiated the narrow, winding coast roads. Laura's heart felt as if it might explode as they reached the turning for his drive. She prayed harder than she had ever prayed before.

As the drive turned she had a clear view of the Georgian house, bathed in the misty, mellow tones of the afternoon sunlight.

Nothing. The house seemed quiet. No child waited on the front step.

Rogan let his breath out in a sigh. 'I was nearly sure…'

Laura felt sick with disappointment.

He turned the car on the gravel drive and stopped. 'Let's just check,' he said quietly.

Together they got out of the car. As they walked around the side of the house they heard low voices.

Laura's heart leapt, then she wondered if she was imagining things because she wanted so much to find the children.

'It was your fault so you should tell him first,' a girl's voice was saying.

They rounded the corner and there, sitting on the back doorstep, were the children.

'Rogan!' They both stood up in surprise. Obviously they had been so busy arguing they hadn't heard the car.

'We weren't expecting you for a while…' Joanne's voice faltered as they saw their mother.

'I don't know whether to kill you or hug you to death,' Laura said shakily. Suddenly she was crying. 'How dare you worry me like this?'

'Oh, Mum!' They both ran to her when they saw her crying. 'We didn't mean to upset you…honestly. We thought we'd get the bus out here and talk to Rogan and he would drive us home before it got too dark. We were going to tell you and Grandma that we were delayed with detention—'

'Never…never do anything like this again. I was so worried…so worried.'

'We're sorry, we're really sorry,' Joanne said in a small, miserable voice when her mother wouldn't stop crying. She looked up at Rogan. 'We just wanted to see you. We didn't mean any harm.'

'I know.' Rogan nodded. 'But you've worried us both sick.' His voice was grim. 'Promise me you'll never do anything like this again.'

'We promise.' Matthew and Joanne spoke in unison, distressed by their mother's tears and Rogan's grave expression.

'OK.' Rogan reached to hug them both.

For a while all four of them stood in a group hug on the back doorstep. Then Rogan straightened.

'Now, then, Matt, Joanne, I think I know what you were going to say to me.'

They both looked up at him expectantly, their eyes shimmering with tears.

'Would you do me the honour of giving me and your mother a few minutes' privacy so we can talk?' he asked seriously.

They nodded and Rogan put an arm around Laura's shoulder. 'I just want one moment…please?' he said to her.

Laura looked up at him. She was so relieved she couldn't stop the tears that were flowing down her cheeks in silent witness of the horrors that had gone through her mind.

'Perhaps we can step inside,' Rogan said, getting out

a key to open the back door. 'Apart from anything else, you should ring the headmistress.'

Joanne and Matthew waited outside. They sat on the step, smiling shyly at Rogan as if they trusted him to put the whole matter back together.

It seemed a million years ago since Laura had been in that kitchen. She took deep breaths and tried to steady herself to make the call to Mrs Buckley.

'Laura.' Rogan's voice stopped her as she looked towards the telephone on the counter-top.

She looked at him questioningly.

'Before you make that call I want to talk to you.'

'Yes, but I should really—'

Rogan caught her hand. 'Laura, this won't wait another minute.'

She was turned to face him.

'I want to tell you something.'

She stared up at him silently.

'I love you,' he said simply.

For a moment she thought she was hearing things.

'I love you, and I've been a complete fool,' Rogan said again. 'Everything you said to me in the office was right. Since the break-up of my marriage I've been afraid of commitment—determined not to be hurt again—but you're right. I can't hide from my feelings and I can't give up on love. I never realised that before. I've never felt this depth of feeling before. I adore you, Laura... I need you.'

Laura swallowed the tears that wanted to flow afresh down her cheeks. She could hardly believe what she was hearing.

'The children were right in a way. I was alarmed by Matthew's statement the other day... I'm ashamed to admit it.' He shook his head. 'I was terrified that I'd hurt them. I sensed their vulnerability—your vulnerability. The sense of responsibility that assailed me took me completely by surprise. I'd never felt so seriously, so intensely, about anyone before—let alone one woman and two children.'

Laura's eyes misted.

'I couldn't believe it when you refused to see me again on Friday night at that party.' Rogan shook his head and took hold of her arms. 'Then when Robert intimated that you and Paul might be an item, might get married, his words had a profound effect. I wanted to grab you and march you out of there. I still don't know how I stopped myself.'

'Maybe something to do with that blonde bombshell you were with?' Laura ventured. 'She was extremely beautiful and, I'm sure, deeply comforting.' She couldn't help the note of sarcasm in her voice. The images she had been conjuring up all weekend of Rogan with that woman still hurt.

'Laura, I couldn't tell you the first thing about her except that her father was a business associate. I didn't arrive with her...and I didn't leave with her.'

'I don't believe you.' Laura stared at him.

'Have I ever lied to you?' he asked her calmly.

She didn't answer him for a moment, then admitted huskily, 'No.'

'Laura, I love you.' Rogan stared down at her. 'And I don't want to lose you. Everything you said to me today was true, except that I only want you because you called the whole thing off. That isn't true. What happened on Friday night just helped to focus my mind. I've never met anyone I've wanted to make a commitment to—until now.'

Laura stared at him. 'Don't say it if you don't mean it,' she said breathlessly.

'I do mean it, Laura.' Rogan touched her face, a kind of wonderment in his dark eyes. 'I love you. I think I have since I first set eyes on you. I tried to fight it, tried to tell myself you were not the wonderful person I kept thinking you were. I was almost actively looking for

excuses to walk away.' He paused. 'But you are wonderful,' he said softly.

'Don't, Rogan.' She found herself crying again.

'Laura, please forgive the cavalier way I've carried
on.' Rogan pulled her closer. 'I want you. I can't imagine life without you now.'

Laura let out her breath in a shuddering sigh. 'I love
you, too. I think I have done since the first moment I
saw you.'

For a while there was silence as they kissed. Laura
poured her heart and soul into the sweetly passionate
caress.

'And you aren't going to see Paul again?' Rogan
asked as he pulled away from her.

'Oh, Rogan, there was never anything between Paul
and I—you know that,' she said with a small laugh.

'No...I wasn't sure. Every damn time he comes to the
office he goes straight to you. I wasn't having it today.
I told the receptionists to tell me the moment he entered
the building.'

Laura's lips curved in a smile of pure astonishment.

'So, what about it?' Rogan asked.

She looked up at him in dazed surprise.

'Will you marry me?' he asked huskily.

'Rogan!' She stared at him. 'I don't think I want to
get married again.'

One dark eyebrow lifted at that. Then he smiled. 'We
are both very similar, aren't we?' he said teasingly.
'Both scared to death of that great institution.'

Laura gave a tremulous smile. 'Wasn't it Mae West
who said she wasn't ready for an institution just yet?'

'Please, Laura.' He said pleadingly. 'I love you, I love
the children. I'll do my best for you all, I promise.'

Laura stared up at him. 'I don't know what to say,'
she whispered, completely overwhelmed.

'Say yes.'

'Your sister isn't going to believe this.' She took a

deep, shuddering breath. 'Rogan, we are from different worlds. You live in America, I live here—'

'What's the small matter of a continent when you're in love?' Rogan grinned and pulled her into his arms.

For a while there was no conversation, just kisses so sweet that they both felt breathless. Then Rogan looked at her. 'When you told me today about your husband I felt I truly understood the shy uncertainty, the sweet vulnerability, I've seen so many times in your eyes. I knew and understood the feelings you generate in me. I'll try never to hurt you, Laura,' he said seriously. 'That's a promise. I only ever want to protect you.'

She smiled gently. 'That goes both ways,' she said shakily.

She looked into his eyes. 'I love you so much. I don't deserve to be this happy.'

'Believe me, you do.' He smiled. 'Now, what do you say? Shall we get married?'

'It's enough that you've asked me.' She shook her head. 'Now that I know you want me, that you love me, it's all I want.'

'But it's not all that I want.' Rogan tipped her face up so that her eyes met his. 'I want everything,' he said quietly. 'I want you, me and the children to be a real family.'

Her heart melted at those words. 'I want that, too,' she whispered…and outside the children moved away from the window and smiled at each other.

MILLS & BOON®

Next Month's Romance Titles

Each month you can choose from a wide variety of romance novels from Mills & Boon®. Below are the new titles to look out for next month from the Presents™ and Enchanted™ series.

Presents™

PACIFIC HEAT	Anne Mather
THE BRIDAL BED	Helen Bianchin
THE YULETIDE CHILD	Charlotte Lamb
MISTLETOE MISTRESS	Helen Brooks
A CHRISTMAS SEDUCTION	Amanda Browning
THE THIRTY-DAY SEDUCTION	Kay Thorpe
FIANCÉE BY MISTAKE	Kate Walker
A NICE GIRL LIKE YOU	Alexandra Sellers

Enchanted™

FIANCÉ FOR CHRISTMAS	Catherine George
THE HUSBAND PROJECT	Leigh Michaels
COMING HOME FOR CHRISTMAS	Laura Martin
THE BACHELOR AND THE BABIES	Heather MacAllister
THE NUTCRACKER PRINCE	Rebecca Winters
FATHER BY MARRIAGE	Suzanne Carey
THE BILLIONAIRE'S BABY CHASE	Valerie Parv
ROMANTICS ANONYMOUS	Lauryn Chandler

On sale from 4th December 1998

H1 9811

Available at most branches of WH Smith, Tesco, Asda, Martins, Borders and all good paperback bookshops

CHRISTMAS

Affairs

MORE THAN JUST KISSES UNDER THE MISTLETOE...

Enjoy three sparkling seasonal romances by your
favourite authors from

MILLS & BOON®
Presents™

HELEN BIANCHIN
For Anique, the season of goodwill has become...
The Seduction Season

SANDRA MARTON
Can Santa weave a spot of Christmas magic for Nick
and Holly in... *A Miracle on Christmas Eve?*

SHARON KENDRICK
Will Aleck and Clemmie have a... *Yuletide Reunion?*

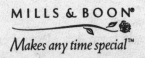

MILLS & BOON®
Makes any time special™

Available from 6th November 1998

Your Special Christmas Gift

Three romance novels from Mills & Boon® to
unwind with at your leisure—
and a luxurious Le Jardin bath gelée to pamper
you and gently wash your cares away.

for just £5.99

Featuring
Carole Mortimer—Married by Christmas
Betty Neels—A Winter Love Story
Jo Leigh—One Wicked Night

MILLS & BOON®

Makes your Christmas time special

Available from 23rd October 1998

HEATHER GRAHAM POZZESSERE

Never Sleep with Strangers

Jon Stuart watched his wife plummet to her death.
Although cleared of any involvement, he endured
years of suspicion. But it was no accident, and he's
now determined to prove it was murder. The prime
suspects are gathered together, and the scene is set
for past and present to collide.

"An incredible story teller!"

—Los Angeles Daily News

1-55166-445-3
**AVAILABLE IN PAPERBACK
FROM NOVEMBER, 1998**

RACHEL LEE

CAUGHT

Someone is stalking and killing women, someone with
a warped obsession. And with loving devotion the
stalker has chosen Kate Devane as his next victim.
What he hasn't realised is that Kate is not alone. She
has a lover. A lover she has never met.

*Rachel Lee takes readers on a "sensational journey
into Tami Hoag/Karen Robards territory."*

–Publishers Weekly

1-55166-298-1
**AVAILABLE IN PAPERBACK
FROM NOVEMBER, 1998**

Barbara DELINSKY

THE DREAM COMES TRUE

For Nina Stone, Crosslyn Rise represents the ultimate coup in her career. There's no limit to what she can do for the secluded complex with her aggressive sales ideas. No limit, that is, except one...John Sawyer.

"When you care to read the very best, the name of Barbara Delinsky should come immediately to mind."

—Rave Reviews

1-55166-175-6
AVAILABLE IN PAPERBACK
FROM NOVEMBER, 1998